OUR
ENVIRONMENT
CAN
BE SAVED

Nelson A. Rockefeller

OUR ENVIRONMENT *CAN* BE SAVED

1970

DOUBLEDAY & COMPANY, INC.
Garden City • New York

AUTHOR'S NOTE

The purpose of this book is to offer a practical man's guide to saving our environment, based on experience rather than theory.

It is dedicated to the proposition that we *can* halt our downhill run toward ecological suicide—and even start climbing back up the slope.

To do this, however, requires more realism on the subject—not more rhetoric. Necessarily, therefore, I have gone into some detail about our environmental efforts in New York State—for these are the practical undertakings I know best.

This book does not presume to be an all-inclusive treatise on so broad a subject. For example, the significant issue of overpopulation is left to more extensive treatment in other works. The focus here is on the record of what we have done, are doing, and plan to do about the air, the water, the land, the power problem, the noise—and the arts.

I'm proud of this record; however, my purpose in presenting it is not pride but pragmatism. If our efforts help others, by guidance, by inspiration, or by warning of the pitfalls, then this book's objective will be achieved.

New York, New York   NELSON A. ROCKEFELLER
July 1970

ACKNOWLEDGMENTS

The author thanks Rodney Campbell and Hugh Morrow for editorial concepts, development, and direction; Berna Gorenstein and Luise Greiner for editorial research; Geoffrey Bartholomew, David Crain, and Linda Gudde for editorial production; Mary Nestor and Nancy Shea for editorial administration and planning.

The author also thanks Kenneth Duskin, Thomas Eichler, John R. Garrison, Alex Gotfryd, Philippe Halsman, John B. Hightower, George W. Humphreys, Stephen Lefkowitz, Thomas W. Losee, Dwight F. Metzler, Gilbert Tauber, Karen Van Westering, Samuel S. Vaughan, and William H. Whyte for their help in the preparation of this book.

The author thanks James G. Cline, Henry L. Diamond, Robert R. Douglass, Alton G. Marshall, Saul Richman, Oscar M. Ruebhausen, and Carol Uht for their help in reviewing the manuscript and for contributing suggestions.

The author thanks the officers and staffs of these organizations of the New York State government for their help in providing material for this book:

Department of State—John P. Lomenzo, Secretary of State; Department of Agriculture and Markets—Don J. Wickham, commissioner; Civil Service Commission—Ersa H. Poston, president; Department of Commerce—Neil L. Moylan, commissioner; Conservation Department—R. Stewart Kilborne, commissioner, which was merged into the Department of Environmental Conservation—Henry L. Diamond, commissioner; Department of Health—Hollis P. Ingraham, commissioner; Department of Education—Ewald B. Nyquist, acting commissioner; State University of New York—Samuel B. Gould, chancellor; Department of Labor—Martin P. Catherwood, industrial commissioner; Department of Transportation—Theodore W. Parker, commissioner; and also:

Office of General Services of the Executive Department—General C. V. R. Schuyler, commissioner; New York State Council of Parks and Outdoor Recreation—Laurance S. Rockefeller, chairman; New York State Historic Trust—Louis C. Jones, chairman, Conrad L. Wirth, former chairman; Office of Planning Coordination—D. David Brandon, director; Public Service Commission—Joseph C. Swidler, chairman; Women's Unit of the Executive Department—Evelyn Cunningham, director; New York State Council on the Arts—Seymour H. Knox, chairman.

———

The author also thanks the officers and staffs of these agencies and commissions who helped provide material for this book:

Port of New York Authority—James C. Kellogg III, chairman; Power Authority of the State of New York—James A. FitzPatrick, chairman; New York State Thruway Authority—R. Burdell Bixby, chairman; New York State Atomic and Space Development Authority—James G. Cline, chairman; Metropolitan Transportation Authority—William J. Ronan, chairman; Hudson River Valley Commission—Fergus Reid III, chairman; Pure Waters Authority—George A. Dudley, chairman, now the

Environmental Facilities Corporation; Agricultural Resources Commission—Gordon L. Conklin, chairman; Urban Development Corporation—George D. Woods, chairman, and Edward J. Logue, president.

———————

The author thanks the officers and staffs of the United States Government and of the specialized agencies of the United Nations and the North Atlantic Treaty Organization who helped in providing material for this book.

———————

The author is finally grateful, for their invaluable help over the years in achieving the record herein described, to: Lieutenant-Governor Malcolm Wilson, Attorney-General Louis J. Lefkowitz, and the leaders and members of the New York State Senate and Assembly.

CONTENTS

FOREWORD

The recently intensified effort to save the environment has succeeded impressively in bringing the subject to wide public notice. It has helped to identify problems and to arouse concern.

But it has been deficient in solutions—and for a very good reason. Effective steps to save the environment will require a highly expert knowledge of governmental machinery, a knowledge of political infighting, a knowledge of how tough and enforceable legislation might be written (and how such legislation has been systematically emasculated in the past). These are subjects that well-intentioned Americans have stubbornly avoided, and by doing so they have all too often condemned themselves to failure in the battle to save the environment.

Governor Rockefeller supplies the missing ingredients. He not only has technical command of the facts of environmental pollution; he is a craftsman in the arts of government. The role of the states in attacking environmental pollution is critically important—and no chief state executive has explored that role more energetically than Governor

Rockefeller. His conception of the battle to save the environment is suitably broad—and his conception of the kinds of governmental approaches that are necessary is equally broad. And innovative. His Urban Development Corporation is one of the most striking innovations in state government in many years.

The effort to save the environment derives much of its political popularity from the impact of immediate personal inconveniences: a sewage-polluted beach, the smog that leaves one's eyes watering, the black granules of soot that drift in through an open window, traffic congestion, noise, ugliness.

But the significance of the current concern for the environment goes much, much deeper than nuisance abatement. It is a belated recognition that as we "succeed" in terms of production, size, speed, growth, the quality of life may deteriorate catastrophically. It is a belated recognition of our oneness with nature, a concern for man himself and his natural environment. It is a belated awareness that our fate as individuals is inseparable from our fate as a species and the future of life on this planet.

Precisely because we have started late we must redouble our efforts to gain command of our situation. We must bring to bear every weapon at our disposal—basic and applied research, public education, and—above all—the kind of skilled governmental action so well illustrated in this book.

July 1970   JOHN W. GARDNER

OUR
ENVIRONMENT
CAN
BE SAVED

ONE

Do It—Together

"I remember as a boy loving sunsets," my father, John D. Rockefeller, Jr., once wrote. "I remember the sunsets from my bedroom window at 4 West 54th Street in New York City, which looked west. I remember what the sycamore trees looked like, and the maple trees. Every time I ride through the woods today, the smell of the trees—particularly when a branch has just been cut and the sap is running—takes me back to my early impressions."

All his life, my father devoted his remarkable energies and his warm sensitivity to the solution of human problems —including what would now be called the protection of the environment. His concept as a philanthropist was the *concentration* of funds and talents and shared endeavors upon major concerns rather than the "scatteration" of money among unrelated deserving causes. My father and his associates in the Rockefeller Foundation invested $500 million in what may now be seen to be historic campaigns. They eradicated hookworm in the southern states, alleviated malaria and yellow fever worldwide, and promoted the education of blacks. They researched, developed, and produced the "miracle" seeds of wheat and rice that offer high hope of success in the current "green revolution" against malnutrition in Asia, Africa, and Latin America.

The boy who loved sunsets grew up into the man who helped to make available to all Americans the beauties of the Grand Teton National Park in Wyoming, the Great Smoky Mountains National Park in North Carolina and Tennessee, and the Acadia National Park around his own home on Mount Desert Island, Maine.

"I have no favorite parks," he once said. "Like your children, you love each of them for different reasons." He fought shoulder-to-shoulder with Henry Fairfield Osborn, John C. Merriam, and Madison Grant, the great conservationists, to save the coastal California redwoods and the sugar pines of Yosemite Valley. Here, too, there was a basic environmental concept. As Fairfield Osborn wrote:

"His actions are curiously symbolic, for much of the wealth that has made possible his munificent contributions for the purpose of conservation has been derived from the depths of the earth. He expresses the completion of a cycle."

Because my father believed, also, that modern man is only part of his history, he helped excavate the Agora, the ancient market place and forum of democracy in Athens, and he helped restore the great Cathedral at Rheims and the château and gardens of Versailles in France. He and his associates restored Colonial Williamsburg in Virginia, an immense project keyed precisely to the original designs. "Always you see something different," he wrote about Williamsburg. "A fence, or a chimney, from some angle you never saw before." In the Sleepy Hollow Restoration in the Hudson River Valley, he purchased and opened up Philipsburg Manor, Van Cortlandt Manor, and Washington Irving's home, Sunnyside, to increase public understanding of American life in the seventeenth, eighteenth, and nineteenth centuries.

Though his personal, artistic interest lay in Chinese por-

celains and medieval tapestries, he not only created The
Cloisters in Fort Tryon Park in Manhattan, but made
frequent donations to the Museum of Modern Art. In
August 1938, *Vogue* magazine described one wonderful
encounter:

"After the coffee at the Rockefeller home, M. Matisse
turned to Mr. Rockefeller and began, half-seriously, to
plead his cause; to explain that the men who had created
the incredibly beautiful green, yellow, red and black por-
celains that were all about us, were really in pursuit of
exactly the same aesthetic goals as those to which Matisse
had personally dedicated himself . . .

"But the philanthropist regretted, in the most polished
French, that he must still appear adamant (even though)
Mrs. Rockefeller, thanks to her very special gifts of persuasion, would eventually wear him down to the consist-
ency of jelly."

Mother, who was one of the founders of the Museum
of Modern Art, did that, and not long afterwards, my father was writing: "I do not find beauty in modern art. I
find instead a desire for self-expression, as if the artist were
saying, 'I'm free, bound by no forms, and art is what flows
out of me.'"

My father's basic environmental concept—at least, the one
that meant the most to me—was also thoroughly modern.
"It was such a beautiful place," he wrote about one park,
"and I wanted to have it opened up so people would see
it."

Father was a development man. He built Rockefeller
Center in the midst of the Great Depression. He bought
and gave to the United Nations the land on which U.N.
headquarters were built in Manhattan. He was an all-out
exponent of economic growth intended to bring prosperity,
health, education, and security to as many people as possible. But he also felt that serenity, equilibrium, the good

life were only to be attained in harmony with nature—
that ecology and the economy ought to be in tune.

Without publicity, my father began in the 1920s to acquire parcels of land on top of the diabase cliffs of the Palisades along the Hudson River in the midst of the New
York metropolitan complex. He suddenly presented seven
hundred acres of prime urban land to the Palisades Park
Commission, as *The New York Times* put it, "to keep them
free of the scars of exploitation."

Father's legacy to our urban civilization was well com-
prehended by Lewis Mumford after a visit to the medieval
museum in The Cloisters:

"A little of that ancient peace still broods over this museum. You can walk around one of these quiet gardens and
even discover whether or not you have a soul. Maybe this
is an experimental model to help us face more cheerfully
the Dark Ages."

Dark Ages then—or now—or both?

"MAN IS DESTROYING HIS OWN ENVIRONMENT"

Given this background, I took office as Governor of New
York in 1959 with an inherited conviction that we *could*
have a productive, prosperous society without destroying
the wholesomeness of our environment. Why should man
create the absurdity of material plenty amid poisoned air,
polluted water, and mountains of solid wastes? I viewed
my responsibility as twofold: to promote human, economic,
and technical progress, but to do so in harmony with the
equally vital necessity to conserve a livable world. My approach was to practice what I called "creative conservation,"
meeting man's needs while protecting his environment. The
difficulty is to maintain a balance between the two.

A governor must go out and fight for new industry and
new jobs. The whole foundation of individual and family
well-being in our industrialized society is jobs—good jobs.

In New York State, total employment had reached record levels in the summer of 1970, with over one million additional jobs created since I took office. Per capita income had increased by 76 per cent. But material progress can exact a high price in terms of nature's gifts—especially in a rapidly expanding, heavily industrialized, and increasingly urban society. Not only the United States but the whole world has recently been waking up to the fact that man is destroying his own environment.

West Germany, well known for its good housekeeping, now produces more than 260 million cubic yards of waste every year. Ten per cent of this is incinerated. The rest of the mess is unloaded into thirty thousand dumps, only one fifth of which are regulated by public health authorities. The Rhine has become Western Europe's sewer, bearing 15.6 million cubic yards of filth into the North Sea every year—and its trout, perch, and salmon are almost all gone. The spic and span Dutch at the river's mouth complain bitterly but, as a *New York Times* reporter noted, they do not use the trash receptacles along the bank. "Everything gets thrown into the Rhine," a Dutchman explained. Another problem for the Netherlands: the famous tulips are damaged by an airborne chemical from steelworks that leaves brown scars on the plants.

Even Communist China's Hsinhua news agency admitted a pollution problem in Shanghai, but discovered, naturally, that this was due to "laissez-faire capitalist-revisionist attitudes." Nevertheless, "the counterrevolutionary trash that put profit in command" has been overcome, Hsinhua assured its readers.

The Soviet Union is currently concerned with the fight to save Lake Baikal, four hundred miles long and six thousand feet deep. The beautiful, wooded shoreline is being encroached upon by new industrial plants—and a new generation of Soviet conservationists is raising a challenge. A three-hour movie, *At the Lake,* shows how Russia's tradi-

tional "develop at all costs" doctrine is being put down a
little in the name of the environment. Actually, almost all
of Russia's rivers are polluted, and the Volga's effluence is
disturbing the ecological balance of the Caspian Sea. And
the Aswan Dam in Egypt—built with Soviet help—is creating new ecological hazards in the Valley of the Nile.

On my mission to the other American republics on behalf of President Nixon in 1969, I found much concern
about the environmental "fallout" of economic development.
Even though some three quarters of the land area of the
American republics is in some form of public ownership,
there is no effective environmental protection. Food production is confined to 5 per cent of the land area in terms
of cultivated crops, mainly on hilly terrain. "Fire and hoe"
agriculture destroys the land. Water resources are ravaged.
The need to conserve grazing lands is only in the first
stages of popular recognition. In my report to the President,
I warned that unless conservation of natural resources was
rapidly undertaken, the increase of the population and the
exploitation of raw materials would make it impossible for
Central and South America to become a region of developed
and self-supporting nations.

As a matter of fact, man is even making a mess of the
moon. In July 1969, Apollo 11 soared away from our littered
land and fouled rivers, up through the polluted atmosphere,
and out through space, touching down 225,000 miles away
on the Sea of Tranquility. This was man's highest technological accomplishment. This was man's apex of individual courage, organizational morale, and the coordination
and cooperation of thousands of people working together.
But left behind on the moon, for the best of technological
reasons, were 5130 pounds of debris—including the lower
stage of the spacecraft, two oxygen containers, two arm-
rests, backpacks, shoes, a water bag, checklists, several still
cameras, a TV camera worth $250,000, and a foodbag weigh-
ing less than one ounce. Also left behind were such pur-

poseful items as a 100-pound seismometer, a 70-pound laser ranging device, the United States Flag-on-the-Moon that thrilled the world, and a silicon disk containing goodwill messages from seventy-three chiefs of state. To date, man has junked more than 37,000 pounds on the moon and there is much more to come. Four burned-out Soviet lunar vehicles and a United States satellite, seven tons in all, are destined to crash into the moon.

The moon will eventually resemble Antarctica, that pure, icebound continent of the South Pole. Antarctica now has smoking garbage dumps, filthy junkyards, and other environmental outrages which, if it can be believed, are to be corrected by a "McMurdo Sound Redevelopment Program." After Antarctica, Australia is the world's cleanest continent. But the Australians were aroused early in 1970 when the popular beach at Maroubra, a suburb of Sydney, had to be closed because of sewage pollution.

However, any American who views the world today with an honest eye can only conclude that the worst mess is in his own backyard. The United States contains less than 6 per cent of the world's population—but it consumes 40 per cent of the world's production and contributes much more than 50 per cent of the world's pollution. Each American in his lifetime uses an average of 26 million gallons of water, 21,000 gallons of gasoline, 10,000 pounds of meat, 28,000 pounds of milk and cream, $6000 worth of clothing, and $7000 worth of furniture. At the very least.

Each year, people in the United States scrap 7 million automobiles and 100 million tires, 20 million tons of paper, 28 billion bottles and 48 billion cans. "Just to collect the garbage costs $2.8 billion a year," *Time* magazine estimates.

Each year, also, United States factories get rid of 165 million tons of solid waste and 172 million tons of smoke, fumes, and other forms of atmospheric pollution. Eighty-three million United States automobiles contribute 60 per cent of air pollution in urban districts. Each year, the

United States paves over a million acres of fields, forests, and exurban green spaces.

Fortunately, and none too soon, saving the environment has become a popular crusade—aided importantly by the energy and concern of young people. Man is beginning to realize that he must drastically alter his pattern of short-sighted abuse of the environment if he wants to survive.

I have been saying this and acting upon this basic assumption ever since I took office as governor. I have believed it ever since I was a boy. In this new crusade, I feel very much as if I am with old friends.

On the one hand, I have tried to prevent and reverse the pollution of the waters, the atmosphere, and the land. This is a colossal undertaking—with much done and much more to be done. On the other hand, I have fought for and won more open spaces and more parks; more forests, historic sites, and scenic wonders accessible to millions; more sources of cultural replenishment everywhere in the state.

Five years ago, New York State pioneered the nation's first truly comprehensive Pure Waters program—with a $1 billion state bond issue to help finance pollution abatement facilities. The total price including private efforts will in time reach four billion dollars—and the federal government, in particular, has a long way to go in meeting its one-third share of the cost. But we already have 363 new sewage plants built or under way in New York State—and we have cracked down on more than one thousand public and private sources of pollution. Sturgeon are beginning to reappear in the Hudson River. Pike and bass are returning to Tonawanda Creek in Western New York. The dissolved oxygen level of the upper East River in Manhattan has increased to a point sufficient to support fish life. Pollution from duck farms on Long Island got so bad a few years back that the state had to close down contaminated shellfish waters; our Pure Waters program has already enabled us to reclaim approximately one third of the underwater lands closed to the harvesting of shellfish. It takes massive effort and enormous sums of money to correct a century of neglect—but it is worth it, and we're doing it.

Four years ago, New York State also launched a far-reaching campaign against atmospheric pollution. Since we started the Clean Air program in 1966, dust pollution of the air is down in 36 of 46 monitored locations all over the state. In New York City, with the worst problem in the state, air pollution by particles is down over 23 per cent; by hydrocarbons, down over 15 per cent; by carbon monoxide, down over 20 per cent. We have also moved against the problem of noise pollution on a major scale.

Our statewide park and recreation land acquisition program has set aside more than 375,000 acres—the equivalent of twenty Manhattan Islands. We initiated a Neighborhood Parks program to make sure that cities and villages could acquire small parks. And we started a $400 million "Next Step" program to develop a variety of outdoor recreational facilities and to make them available to all New Yorkers.

In sum, we have added forty-three new state parks to our inventory, and park attendance has risen by 50 per cent. No fewer than forty-two million people visited New York State parks in 1969. The value of recreation to the physical and mental well-being of so many millions is, to me, a key element of environmental protection.

Yet the quality of the individual's life depends on more than his physical surroundings. The arts, in particular, increasingly fulfill a spiritual need in our mechanized industrial age.

I believe that the arts are not for the privileged few—they are for the many, for the people as a whole. This is the unusual strength of the arts in America. The availability of cultural opportunities is also an important force in attracting job-producing industries to the state. It all ties together. And so we founded the first State Council on the Arts in the nation. Last year alone, the council sponsored nearly a thousand musical and theatrical performances and art exhibitions everywhere in the state, from rural communities to the ghettoes. The state legislature appropriated almost $20 million for these activities in the current fiscal year, with some $18 million of this earmarked specifically as state aid to financially ailing cultural institutions—symphony orchestras, performing arts companies, museums, and others.

What all this adds up to is that nowhere else in the United States has so much been done to protect the environment and to enhance the quality of life.

Yet the more I work on the problem, the more certain I am of the wisdom contained in that famous saying of Pogo, the comic strip character:

"We have met the enemy, and he is us."

The ecologist, LaMont C. Cole, of Cornell University, puts it this way:

"The message that the ecologists seek to impart could hardly be more urgent and important. So it is that man, in the process of seeking a better way of life, is destroying the natural environment that is essential to any kind of human life at all; that, during his time on earth, man has made giant strides in the direction of ruining the arable land upon which his food supply depends, upsetting the delicate chemical and climatic balances upon which his very existence depends. There is all too little indication that man has any intention of mending his ways."

SIGNS OF HOPE

Happily, the ecological skies are brightening. President Nixon keyed his 1970 State of the Union message to the new crusade. "Shall we surrender to our surroundings," he asked, "or shall we make our peace with nature and begin to make reparations for the damage we have done to our air, to our land, and to our water?" Three weeks later, in a special message to Congress on the environment, President Nixon called for "expanded government action" in water pollution and air pollution controls, solid waste disposal, and the increase of park lands and open spaces.

The President said there should be nationwide air pollution standards for industry, more stringent regulations governing automobile emissions, and $10,000-per-day fines, if necessary, for municipalities and industries that failed to meet federal air and water quality levels. The President indicated he favored the eventual elimination of tetraethyl lead from automobile fuels and he initiated a federal research and development program to develop a car that would be "virtually pollution free."

President Nixon's most notable specific was a $10 billion program for the construction of municipal waste treatment plants in a national pure waters campaign. This would be similar in concept to New York's five-year-old Pure Waters program. The federal government would allocate $4 billion of this sum, over four years. There would be an additional financing mechanism in which municipalities would be assured a market for $6 billion in municipal bonds.

Unfortunately, this sum is hopelessly inadequate. If New York State's Pure Waters program alone will cost over $3 billion in state, local, and federal government funds, President Nixon's program will need, realistically, something in the region of at least $30 billion. The presidential commitment is vitally important, however.

In 1970 the President signed a Water Quality Improvement Act increasing the fines for oil spills and the liability for the cost of cleaning up the mess. He also signed a bill creating a new Commission on Population Growth. In one week the Justice Department filed suit to enjoin the Florida Power and Light Company from thermal pollution of Miami's Biscayne Bay, indicted United States Steel Corporation and one of its plant managers for polluting Lake Michigan, filed criminal charges against ten large companies for discharging oil and oily substances into Lake Michigan. Meanwhile, the Department of Health, Education and Welfare put out new air pollution criteria for the measurement of harmful carbon monoxide, and the Atomic Energy Commission sought tighter curbs on discharges of air and water from nuclear power plants.

On another occasion, the President issued a five-page executive order to federal agencies to comply with state water and air pollution standards within three years. As an ardent advocate of the federal system, President Nixon would be the first to agree that he is racing to keep up with the states. For example:

In Washington State, Governor Daniel J. Evans required strip mining companies to file plans for restoring the landscape. He set up an advisory agency on the siting of power plants, created a Department of Ecology, assigned unlimited liability to oil companies for oil spills even in cases of "Act of God."

In Georgia, Governor Lester G. Maddox received a major conservation measure, passed by both houses of the legislature, creating a Coastal Marshlands Protection Agency. The idea was to stop phosphate mining in the marshes that had been imperiling the shrimp.

In Maine, Governor Kenneth M. Curtis signed legislation providing for state control of the siting of all major commercial and industrial developments. In Massachusetts, Governor Francis W. Sargent, a professional conservationist, was considering a bill to allow individual citizens to bring suit to stop any form of damage to the environment whatever.

In California, the state attorney-general sued the commanding general of Fort Ord for dumping undisinfected sewage into Monterey Bay, asking $6000 per day for every day the Army did not cease and desist. "If we succeed, we will set a model for the rest of the country," the state said, and this was indeed a major case.

BUSINESS JOINS THE CRUSADE

United States business showed signs of reversing the attitude which had long put profits ahead of protection of the environment. Top management began to listen more intently to the long-neglected public affairs departments and public relations directors who had been advocating environmental protection for years. At a conference on water pollution, one steel company chief executive said, "We can't put any money into pollution control that we haven't first made as profits." To which another chief executive replied, "Pollution control isn't an out-of-profit item. It's part of the cost of production."

Donald C. Cook, president of the American Electric Power Company, struck another note when he said, "It is one thing to say a utility company must spend $100 million on air pollution control equipment. It is another for the customers to realize that their electric bills must increase by $15 million a year to make this expenditure possible." Frank R. Barnett, chairman of the Union Pacific Railroad, predicted that government will eventually do most of the antipollution work, with private enterprise doing the rest and passing on the cost to the consumer. George E. Keck, president of United Air Lines, held that the cost of pollution control will be accepted by industry "in the same way safety is accepted."

The inevitable transition pains for United States business were beginning to be felt. The Portland Cement Company phased out a sixty-five-year-old plant at Egypt, Pennsylvania, rather than spend $1 million to upgrade its facilities in conformance to Pennsylvania's air pollution laws. Jones and Laughlin Steel Corporation threatened to close parts of its iron foundry in Pittsburgh. Two lumber companies, a feed supplement plant, and a lime plant closed in Texas under pressure from the Texas Air Control Board.

Officials of United States Steel said they might have to close down their fifty-five-year-old plant in Duluth, the largest single employer in the city, because Minnesota state officials were demanding that it comply with new air and water quality standards.

In Houston, civic authorities warned a chemical company to reduce its emission of industrial wastes. The company hired a public relations firm and proposed to repair its image in Houston by joining in charity work, contributing to the symphony, setting up company sports teams, and so forth. After measuring the climate, however, the public relations men told the company to spend its money on antipollution devices instead, and the company did.

The National Industrial Conference Board reports that pollution control spending by 248 typical companies rose 23 per cent in 1969. Nondurable goods industries doubled their environmental spending in a year, and textile producers quadrupled it. The motor vehicle and equipment industry increased its investment in antipollution devices in 1969 by 195 per cent. The NICB's index companies alone spent $255 million in 1969—and no one knows how much private enterprise as a whole is devoting to the problem nationwide.

Republic Steel Corporation has committed $100 million to pollution control—with $40 million in major construction currently under way. Thomas F. Patton, chairman, says, "The need for improving the quality of air and water has been accepted as a continuing responsibility with a very high priority. Over the last decade, we have installed no new production facility without the latest pollution controls, and we will continue this policy. Fighting pollution created by older plants is a more complicated and costly problem. To solve this, without economic dislocation and unemployment, and yet continue to make progress, will require cooperation and understanding from regulatory agencies."

The new pollution technology is, in itself, a new opportunity for United States business. Large firms are moving to compete with the small, specialist makers of pollution control equipment who have watched their own sales increase tenfold. As the president of a small water purifying company said recently, "Everybody else has discovered the business we've been in for years."

Labor unions are making statements hailing the new concern for the environment. These unions include the United Auto Workers, the Oil, Chemical, and Atomic Workers, the Teamsters, the Amalgamated Clothing Workers, the United Sheetmetal Workers, and others. One Chicago local of the Operating Engineers said its members would not work on a construction project in which two million gallons of oil and sludge were to be dumped into Lake Michigan: "Local 150 intends to let all contractors know that we will no longer tolerate pollution of the environment."

Bankers and lawyers are getting involved—and this is also extremely important. In Maine the executive committees of three statewide banking associations have accepted a new Bankers' Pollution Code. This is a voluntary proposal for bankers to weigh an industry's attitude toward and performance in the environment before making loans. More than a hundred financial institutions are members, and the code is said to be the first such adopted by a state. Lending officers have been told in effect that they have a key role in safeguarding the environment of Maine.

The International Bank for Reconstruction and Development has said that, henceforth, ecological considerations must be weighed in international development projects. This could specifically affect a proposal to finance the construction of a hydroelectric plant at Murchison Falls, in Uganda, Africa. Most of the Africans there want the plant, and clearly prefer it to undisturbed wildlife. This might become a classic ecology-economy test case in the underdeveloped world.

It is true that the peoples of the developing countries are more interested in food and jobs, the dignity of labor, better living standards, health and education, than they might be in protection of the environment. Theodore Roosevelt might have termed this "prosperity at any price." But all this will be swiftly changed once survival is seen to be at stake in intelligent conservation measures.

In Princeton, New Jersey, not long ago, sixty United States lawyers and other leaders in professional life met to found a new group entitled The National Resources Defense Council, Inc. This organization has been formed to function in the environmental field much as the American Civil Liberties Union operates in the field of individual rights. Among its sponsors are the National Audubon Society, the Beinecke Foundation, Christian Herter, Jr., New York lawyer Stephen Duggan, and the *Christian Science Monitor*'s eminent Erwin D. Canham. Among its directors are John B. Oakes, editorial page editor of *The New York Times,* Mrs. Louis Auchincloss, and Dr. Gifford B. Pinchot.

One hundred seminars on environmental law are now being offered in United States law schools. New volumes are being published by lawyers on the legal niceties and intricacies of the earth. The lawsuits are already pouring in. In Phoenix, Arizona, two university professors and their wives are seeking $2 billion in damages from six copper companies that operate almost all the copper smelters in the state. The plaintiffs want this money to be divided among 700,000 residents of the Salt River Valley because the smoke from the smelters is injurious to health and damages the beauty of the environment. A woman in New York is filing suit in federal court against eight DDT manufacturers on behalf of "all the people in the United States" and "generations yet unborn." She is claiming $30 billion. Most of the lawsuits are more realistic. Everybody is questing for the perfect test case.

THE YOUTH COMMITMENT

Powering the crusade to save the environment—and prodding whenever it falters—is an upsurge of concern on the part of America's youth. The same sense of commitment that drew millions of young people into the struggle for equal rights for blacks, into the 1968 presidential election campaigns, into the protests against the war in Vietnam, is now engaged on a planetary scale. This is a thrilling development.

The new youth action is distinctive, first, in its sincerity, its virtual absence of phoniness. Young men and women have demanded, and obtained, new courses and even new departments of ecology in almost all United States colleges. More than a hundred colleges have set up interdepartmental centers to coordinate the teaching of many aspects of environmental planning. Universities are working on joint programs with public health, sanitary engineering, city planning, and other agencies of state and local government, industry, and private research organizations. The University of Southern California, the University of Michigan, the University of Wisconsin, Cornell University, and Johns Hopkins University are among the institutions which have recently created independent ecological bodies.

Union College in Schenectady, New York, is typical in its interdisciplinary dialogue. A weekly "existence seminar" is directed by a professor of mechanical engineering. "Too many current approaches attack just one area," he said, "and they result in a thousand solutions to the same problem. Everybody is so polarized in their fields that it's difficult to find common ground." So the group is designing and dry-running a functional city in which coordinated answers to the problems are sought.

Another Union College professor is conducting a course in noise pollution. His students are all over the region, measuring the sound levels of industry, transportation, and even snowmobiles. The new snowmobile boom has brought money, excitement, and the deafening racket of exhausts to the colder, northern areas of the state. The students are attempting to find out whether the noise of the snowmobiles is having adverse effects on hibernating animals—not to mention the residents.

A third Union College professor has a course on "Inland Water Pollution from Recreational Boating." His students are interviewing marine operators and boat owners, researching the problems caused by motorboat engines, trash thrown overboard, shoreline camps, and human wastes from boats.

The interaction of students and faculty has worked well in the environmental field. "It's amazing how quickly it's caught on," said an assistant professor of systems ecology at Yale University. "Not long ago you had to defend your discipline if you were an ecologist. Now they're getting you to speak at teach-ins. Teach-in! I've been teaching in for years, and they're just discovering it." Yale's Forestry School is working with a five-year $1 million grant it recently received from the Ford Foundation. And Yale has attracted liberal arts students to the sciences by starting a new course entitled "Biology and Human Affairs." Three hundred and twenty students enrolled for it—quite a start.

The National Environment Teach-in on April 22, 1970, was, to me, not only a passionate display of commitment, but an extremely useful and helpful experience. I directed the State Health, Education, Conservation, and other departments to provide speakers and materials for the teach-in. I took this occasion to sign the bill creating the state's new Department of Environmental Conservation, the hard, new cutting-edge of the state's crusade for a better environment. We also set up a new system for clearing information and ideas developed by the students that we could put to use.

It was, in fact, a teach-in for millions everywhere. One of my air pollution technicians reported:

"Individual citizens are now entering the battle by the thousands—through their clubs, churches, and local conservation groups. They are involved—students, professors, businessmen, farmers, housewives. They are informed, and they are interested in power."

The second distinctive aspect of the new youth action, in my judgment, is more profound. I have long watched the growing disenchantment of millions of young people with my generation's life style. I believe that I have understood. As one of my young volunteer political workers put it:

"The great silent majority, alike in manner, mind, and morals, has been content with life in a box. But youth in America finds very little appeal in the grand suburban ideal of our parents. We do not understand the senseless vacancy. Young people look around today and ask, Why? Why do we want? Why do we contaminate? Why are we living as we are? What is it about the magical dollar bill that is supposed to bring instant happiness? What is so desirable about the sad and sour effects of having too much?

"Should we bother to clean up the atmosphere which penetrates a deteriorating society? I believe we should. Life itself is of infinite value. Examine a flower one morning while walking through a sunlit field. Climb a mountain and admire the life and love that emanates from every living creation, abundantly perpetuated by a balance of nature.

"Pessimism is a state of mind that should not exist amid the beauty of a world that is harmoniously relevant. Nature is a haven. It represents the existence of love. You cannot buy beauty. It is there. It is free, and it grows."

New York State has a new environmental organization, entitled ABATES, short for Ambassadors to Bring Action Through Environmental Study. It now has two thousand active "salesmen" in more than a hundred study groups throughout the state. It coordinates its activities with the American Association of University Women, the Federation of Garden Clubs, the League of Women Voters, the New York State Conservation Council, the Federation of Home Bureaus, the Congress of Parents and Teachers, the Federation of Women's Clubs and the State Grange.

A statewide Action for Clean Air Committee has more than three thousand active members in thirty-five counties. An Environmental Health Council has been set up in Albany, the state capital, to provide an outlet through which these community proposals may be channeled and measures acted upon. Another group, Citizens for Clean Air, has twenty-five hundred members agitating against atmospheric pollution in New York City.

I think it is wonderful that students are coming together with suburbanites, businessmen with academicians, in what is beginning to look like a transcendent issue. I think it is marvelous that we have found something that can unite us. It has been a long, long time.

We must achieve an interplay of popular pressures and enthusiasm, the precise application of sizable funds and technological skills, and the wise action of government at all the levels of our federal system. That means federal, state, and local governments working closest to the problems they understand the most. That means working together in a spirit reminiscent of America's pioneer days.

But it also means toughness where toughness is needed— and those industries or other polluters of the environment with a "don't give a damn" attitude will find me an unyielding adversary.

I believe our environment *can* be saved. I believe this is a *unifying* issue for the whole country—now so sadly and so needlessly polarized. I believe we can and must do it *together*.

TWO

Cleaning Up the Atmosphere

While polluted air almost never appears on a death certificate, medical research strongly implicates it as a contributing cause of many deaths. Polluted air influences health gradually, so its effects are extremely difficult to pinpoint. However, mounting evidence indicates a steady, steep increase in the incidence of such respiratory diseases as asthma, bronchitis, lung cancer, and emphysema. Cities with an abundance of air pollution have the greatest incidence of these diseases.

A New York City medical examiner described the health effects of air pollution in these stark words: "On the autopsy table, it's unmistakable. The person who has spent his life in the mountains has nice pink lungs. The city dweller's are as black as coal."

The new war against air pollution should be considered part of the war against cancer, says Dr. Jonathan E. Rhoads, president of the American Cancer Society. Authorities may argue that cigarette smoking is more dangerous than general air pollution as a cause of lung cancer. But as Dr. Robert Horton puts it, speaking from his experience as chief of the federal government's Health Effects Research Program:

"What we do know is that people get killed by air pollution, and I don't see any excuse for there being enough air pollution to kill people. Do you?"

Fortunately, the state of our technology is already such that our skies *can* be made cleaner. Progress is being made. Much more needs to be done. And it is everybody's fight—for pollution affects everybody, and it can happen anywhere.

A New York State Department of Conservation helicopter took off from Albany not long ago on an unusual kind of spy-in-the-sky reconnaissance. The helicopter's mission was to scout for violations of our New York State Health Rule 187, which limits the type and the amount of atmospheric pollution released by industrial plants. On board were Alexander Rihm, Jr., State Assistant Health Commissioner; Harry Hovey, associate director of the Division of Air Resources; Jack Lauber, a specialist air control engineer, and Peg Breen, the environment columnist for the Albany *Knickerbocker News*.

The helicopter headed first for the Atlantic Cement Company's $45 million plant at Ravena, New York. A large cloud of steam and cement dust was rising from a single smokestack and dust was settling on trees and on a junkyard for abandoned automobiles. The air control engineer said the plant had an electrostatic precipitator for controlling the dust emission that was "theoretically 99.6 per cent effective," but the company was having problems maintaining efficiency. That single stack could also, theoretically, emit 35,000 pounds of cement dust over the neighborhood every hour.

This plant was in the news because it was the center of a test case with national significance in environmental law. The Court of Appeals, the highest tribunal in the state, was enjoining the company from committing a "nuisance" to the public in the form of smoke and cement dust pollution. The court reversed two lower court rulings in part, holding that it was acting in the public interest "because of the public concern with air pollution arising from many sources in industry and in transportation."

The court also imposed a financial sanction against the company—which supports three hundred local jobs and pays local taxes. The firm was ordered to pay $185,000 in permanent damages.

The company was, however, not otherwise restrained— and New York State's Attorney-General Louis J. Lefkowitz promptly moved into the situation. He termed the court's ruling akin to "granting the cement company a virtual lease to pollute the air." Lefkowitz urged new legislation requiring his office to be notified so it could participate in the public interest in similar cases in the future. Meanwhile, the state's watch was on the company to see what it would do to police itself. There were plans for new water sprays, a new dust dump, and a new dust collection system which would cost the company more than $1 million.

The helicopter flew next to an Allegheny Ludlum Steel Corporation plant at Watervliet, which was also in the news. The plant belched a reddish dust cloud of iron oxide as the helicopter approached. The air control engineer explained this was due to the addition of pure oxygen to the steel manufacturing process. Recently, the state health commissioner, Dr. Hollis Ingraham, had come under attack for granting Allegheny Ludlum a six-month extension on the date by which it must award a contract for the installation of antipollution equipment. But Dr. Ingraham said that the alternative to the extension was a plant shutdown throwing two hundred people out of work.

The helicopter flew next to the huge General Electric Company installations at Schenectady. The air control engineer said this company had been "very cooperative" with the state's health rules. GE had submitted reports on the emissions of each of its divisions and was taking action against violators on its own. The company had invited the

Health Department of the state to conduct a special sampling process at a silicone plant. GE had several scrubbers designed to control potential toxic pollution at the plant and wanted our health experts to verify the effectiveness of the new equipment.

The Penn Dixie Cement Company near Howe Cave in Schoharie County was another example of "high control" of atmospheric pollution, the air control engineer said as the helicopter flight continued. This company had recently installed a new technological process for minimizing dust and had attained 99 per cent effectiveness. But the Portland Cement Company's plant at Glens Falls, New York, was "antiquated" in terms of dust control, according to the engineer. Its three kilns emitted more than 2100 pounds of cement dust every hour. However, the company has since submitted formal plans for a $1,600,000 pollution abatement project to the New York State Health Department. These plans included the removal of the three tallest industrial smokestacks in the northern part of the state and the installation of an electrostatic precipitator. Two new, smaller smokestacks would reduce emissions to acceptable levels. Thus this serious source of pollution was on its way to being removed.

In the Albany area alone, fifty major polluters representing several hundred sources of air pollution were expected to be under atmospheric pollution controls before the end of 1970. This progress results from a first-of-its-kind air resources master plan the state has completed for the eighteen county region centering on Albany, a plan we consider destined to serve as a model for the state and for the nation. Almost all open burning of junked cars has been prohibited. More than half of the region's refuse disposal facilities have been brought under strict regulation, with the remainder soon to follow.

More than a thousand industries statewide are complying, voluntarily, with the atmospheric pollution guidelines and requirements of the state. Abatement of filthy air in New York is, in fact, making visible progress. New York's state and local governments lead the nation in funds committed to air pollution control, with more than 17 per cent of the national total. More than six thousand firms submitted the specific data we needed to help us draw up abatement standards for the many different types of air pollution—and they did it more than a year in advance of the official deadline.

Even in New York City, famed worldwide for the dirt that gets into people's eyes, there has been dramatic improvement that has gone largely unappreciated. Mayor John V. Lindsay once quipped after a trip to the Rocky Mountains that he wasn't used to breathing air he could not see. But since 1966 the amount of sulfur dioxide pollution of the atmosphere in New York City is down dramatically, most notably because Consolidated Edison converted to low-sulfur fuels three years ahead of deadline.

On the other hand, the Citizens for Clean Air said not long ago that they had lost faith "in any quick action" through court or governmental processes against New York City apartment incinerators that were contaminating the atmosphere. Mrs. Linda Fosburg, executive director of the citizens' group, said there might be moves "to nag the power structure." There might be stickers on the doors of individual landlords, or pickets parading outside the buildings, even rent strikes.

The fact was that, in the spring of 1970, no fewer than four hundred landlords had obtained injunctions against a city air pollution law calling for the upgrading or discontinuance of nuisance incinerators.

The compliance rate in New York City was only 18 per cent for private incinerators and 20 per cent for public housing, school, and other installations. The costs of the new equipment, the difficulties of new technology were among the problems, and the city government was planning a television teach-in of some thirty thousand building service employees on how to run oil burners and incinerators with less pollution. One large apartment development switched from incinerators to compactors for its refuse, and reported that tenants were out on their terraces in fine weather, no longer complaining about fly ash in their eyes.

The Citizens for Clean Air identified what they considered to be the five major polluters in the city as the city's own Housing Authority, the New York Real Estate Board, the Metropolitan Life Insurance Company, the taxicab industry, and—still everybody's pet peeve—Consolidated Edison.

But whenever the costs and the technology were right, there were frequent instances of cooperation and results in New York City. Transit Authority buses, once notoriously smoky and long a favorite target of complaint by New York City's dwellers, are now actually among the cleanest-operating vehicles in the city. Three out of every four of the 4285 Transit Authority buses have been equipped with improved needle-type fuel injection systems. These buses also now use the best quality of diesel fuel available. The diesel engine updating, premium fuel, and improved maintenance combine to reduce smoke emissions by more than 75 per cent, and the last bus engine will be updated by July 1971. The changes have cost the Transit Authority $217,073 annually for injector conversions and $105,000 for the extra fuel cost. Every bus in New York City is, in fact, checked every day for smoke emissions and excessive lubricating oil consumption. If more than one quart of lubricating oil is consumed in thirty-five miles of operation, the bus is put in the shop for repairs. All Transit Authority personnel are under orders to report smoking buses. Long-range alternatives to diesel engines such as gas turbines and electric buses are also being investigated.

In truth, the Transit Authority and its state-sponsored parent, the Metropolitan Transportation Authority, are major influences for the reduction of air pollution by expansion of electrified rail service. Under MTA, the city's subway system is being extended for the first time in forty years, as well as being modernized. MTA also is planning underground "people mover" systems, such as moving sidewalks, horizontal escalators, and small-wheel vehicles in the New York City financial district. None of these would be run by pollution-producing power systems.

THE AUTOMOBILE AND AIR POLLUTION

In New York State, in the United States, the number one cause of atmospheric pollution is of course the automobile. Some perspective is needed on this subject. The automobile is indeed a polluter and a killer. The accident death rate from automobiles is currently in excess of fifty-five thousand people every year. The automobile creates traffic jams in the cities and junkyards in the countryside. Sociologists say the family car has made possible not only the spread of the suburbs but the abandonment of central cities by the very people who could afford to pay taxes to solve the problems. But motor vehicle transportation is essential to the current economy of the United States—and few contemporary Americans would willingly give up its convenience in any event. Plainly, the solution lies in further "civilizing" the automobile—and steady progress is being made.

In 1962 I signed into law a requirement that all motor vehicles in New York State be fitted with crankcases designed to reduce air pollution. This was one of the first such measures in the nation. Each year, these restrictions alone now keep some 150,000 tons of hydrocarbons out of the atmosphere.

In 1966 we won the overwhelming approval of the state legislature for a comprehensive Clean Air program that required antipollution devices on motor vehicle exhaust systems as federal regulations also now require.

Since the federal emission controls began with the 1968 model automobiles—and only 10 per cent of the 100 million vehicles in the United States are replaced annually—it will take about eight more years for the controls to become entirely effective. There is also concern about how valid the testing of new automobiles may be. Manufacturers currently "average" tests of cars coming off the assembly line. California intends to require a 100 per cent test, a fairly massive undertaking. General Motors recently announced it had developed an antipollution system that could be installed on pre-1966 cars at a cost of approximately $35, to be put on the market late in 1970.

General Motors currently is redesigning its automobile engines to operate efficiently on unleaded gasoline. Lead is a pollutant, comprising much of the particulate matter in exhaust fumes. Most of GM's 1971 models will be affected by the design changes, and perhaps all of the 1972 models. The current high-performance automobiles, which need high-octane fuels, will be subject to thorough redesign. The automobile companies may be able to redesign big car engines so they will operate as efficiently on unleaded fuel, or oil companies may be able to develop high-octane fuel with less lead or no lead. There may be both. Or drivers may have to do with less horsepower, less acceleration, and lower mileage per gallon than is now the case.

Major oil companies have boarded the bandwagon—and estimates range up to $3 billion as to the costs of the oil industry's efforts to take the lead out of gasoline.

Who is to pay for all these environmental expenditures? Gilbert B. Phillips, president of the Automobile Club of New York, said that new car buyers would be spending $2 billion per year for pollution control devices starting in 1973 and "it will be the largest annual investment a single consumer group has ever been asked to make in the area of environmental control." In California, however, gasoline still costs much the same as it did before the gasoline companies began to pay out large sums for pollution controls in their plants and products. What is absorbed by the companies—and their stockholders—and what is passed on to the consumers is the basic question.

Henry Ford II says that automobile pollution is already under better control and is closer to final solution than any other major aspect of the environmental crisis. He speaks with authority, as an employer of outstanding research engineers and as an industrialist of noteworthy social concern.

Eventually, the internal combustion engine may well give place to other forms of propulsion. However, work on the electric, steam, and hybrid gasoline-natural gas powered automobiles has not proceeded very far. "The fact is that no one has yet invented a replacement which has adequate performance, reliability, and safety, or which can be produced at a reasonable cost and requires a minimum of maintenance," says Dr. Lee DuBridge, presidential science adviser. The Nixon administration is supporting research in this field.

New York, along with other states, is also moving along a cooperative path toward reducing atmospheric pollution caused by the air transportation industry. The Air Transport Association says that only 1 per cent of the nation's air pollution is caused by jet planes. The concentration near large airports, however, is much more than that.

State Attorney-General Lefkowitz recently sought court action to expedite the timetable for the installation of anti-pollution devices on jet aircraft engines. The federal government and the airlines had set that date as "late 1972." Within one month of Lefkowitz's initiative, United Air Lines announced a $3 million engine-cleaning program on a speeded-up schedule. Thirty other airlines operating in the New York area were expected to follow suit. Attorney-

General Lefkowitz also sued eleven foreign-owned airlines to stop their contribution to air pollution near Kennedy Airport.

Refitting the jet engines will cost nine major domestic airlines alone more than $30 million. For an industry in the midst of severe growing pains, cost inflation, and one of the worst profit squeezes in its brief history, the willingness to comply with our initiative is remarkable. It demonstrates that the drive to clean our skies in the 1970s is being taken very seriously indeed.

NEW YORK STATE ACCEPTS THE CHALLENGE

If I might seem to be optimistic about the prospects for cleaning up the atmosphere, it is because I have seen what happens when industries, municipalities, and citizens' groups work together to solve the problems in New York State. We did much to get the ball rolling in the 1960s— but nothing could have happened if the public had not wanted it to.

In my first year as governor, we established a fifteen-station statewide sampling network to measure air pollution. This has now grown to more than two hundred stations. In 1961 we established a "smog alert" system to provide early warning of serious pollution. In 1962 we adopted new rules requiring anybody who wanted to build a plant in the state, or modify an existing one, to obtain the permission of the State Air Pollution Control Board.

In 1964 we developed the first system in the nation for zoning air appropriate to its "best use." We set standards of air purity for rural, residential, commercial, and industrial zones. Now, more than 85 per cent of the people in the state live under this atmospheric zoning. We have standards for measuring violations, and we take enforcement action against the polluters. On the other hand, our state Public Health Law also provides 50 per cent reimbursement to local governments for health programs including air pollution controls.

In 1966 our new Clean Air Program granted tax exemptions for industries that installed pollution control equipment. It offered 100 per cent state aid for the planning of municipal solid waste disposal systems. Violators of the Air Pollution Control Board regulations were made subject to a maximum initial fine of $1000 plus $200 for each day the violation continued.

In New York, then, we have accepted the challenge to clean our skies and achieve for ourselves and our children a more livable world. This is a battle which must be pursued on every front—sometimes in the most unlikely places.

Take Arkville, New York, for an example. Arkville rests on the western hip of the Catskills, in a land of deer and trout, picturesque mountains and regrowing forests. In 1963 Arkville had little left. The houses needed paint, the stores were mostly closed, and the remaining railroad track— three freights a week—was so rickety the diesel crew said they rode ready to jump. But there were still a few guest-houses in the hills, and in one of them stayed an English visitor who had been coming to the town for seven years. He was asked how he liked the town. "Not much to it," he said. "That's what I like. Quiet and relaxing." And he added, "Since the diesel engine replaced the steam engine on the railroad, the air is absolutely Number One Pure."

Then disaster struck in Arkville. A woodworking plant in town began to use a tepee burner to dispose of scraps and rubble. A tepee burner is a tall iron cone, resembling an Indian wigwam, that emits a great deal of smoke. Suddenly, Number One Pure Air became smog in the streets. Arkville was so small that the smoke absolutely blanketed the town all the way out to the five horses in the north pasture and Nat Greene's goats on Blueberry Hill.

Arkville people who had hoped for more tourist business over the years were furious. Although it was against local principle to dicker with "government," they finally protested to the State Department of Health. This led to a series of investigations, tests, verifications, documentation of violations, meetings, correspondence, and hearings. One elder citizen commented, "Those bureaucrat fellers just talk and tax." "No," said a high school student, who was paid little attention because he wore longish hair, "they have a procedure to follow."

After first attempting persuasion and negotiation, the Health Department held a formal hearing on the Arkville burning tepee and obtained a stipulation calling for an end to the use of the burner. The burning of refuse was to be stopped and diverted, preferably to an approved incinerator or a sanitary landfill. The smoke pollution in Arkville ended. The tall iron cone stands cold and black. The air once again is Number One Pure.

Another interesting pollution case involved one of the Iroquois Indians of New York State, Mr. Benny Schenandoah.

On the Onondaga Reservation, south of Syracuse, Benny Schenandoah ran an auto parts operation and dump. It was an open-burning dump, and the smoke added to air pollution over nearby homes and reached the southern rim of the city.

In 1968 there were angry citizens' complaints. The nuisance of the smoke and smell was verified, the violations were recorded, and a State Health Department man suggested to Mr. Schenandoah that he put out the fires. The Iroquois protested that this was his livelihood. The health inspector said that regulations must be obeyed, and compiled the necessary papers.

The file moved along channels to Albany and upward to the Attorney-General's office. There were many legal pages entitled: Hollis S. Ingraham (the State Health Commissioner) versus Benny Shenandoah (the C in Benny's name was lost, but not missed). Involved now, in addition to Dr. Ingraham, were Attorney-General Lefkowitz; Dunton F. Tynan, Assistant Solicitor-General; John Hathorn, State Adviser on Indian Affairs; Donald A. MacHarg, counsel of the Department of Health, and their aides and staffs and troops. Mr. Schenandoah told them all he would continue to run his dump in his own way. "It's my living . . ." he said.

Then someone in the Office of Counsel had an idea. The Chiefs of the Onondaga Council, the heirs of the Onondagas of the Iroquois Confederacy, were brought into the case against Schenandoah. An ordinary action of the Division of Air Resources, allowing for legal maneuvers, might have taken a long time. But the Chiefs of the Onondaga Council met at once to consider the problem—and they issued the following resolution on March 28, 1968:

> *At A Special Meeting Held By The Chiefs Of The Onondaga Council It Was Resolved That Benny Schenandoah Will Have Until April 15, 1968 To Burn The Refuse At His Refuse Site. It Was Also Resolved That All Dumping Will Cease On April 1, 1968. There Will Be A $100 Fine For Anyone Dumping After April 1, 1968.*

The Onondaga chiefs informed the state government in an accompanying letter that:

(1) Chiefs would be stationed at the dump to inform people that there would be no more dumping.

(2) A sign would be placed at the entrance of the dump saying there would be no more dumping.

(3) Benjamin Schenandoah himself would park a truck across the driveway so that no trucks could enter the dump.

". . . the Chiefs have their own method of enforcing rules . . ." a Health Department internal memo said.

In a further memorandum closing the action file, an attorney at the Division of Air Resources noted:

"Mr. Shenandoah (still no C) is an excellent example of an advanced, civilized approach toward the orderly, rapid solution of environmental problems. The Iroquois should be commended and we should follow their example."

An example of citizen cooperation against air pollution on a grander scale may be found in the Health Department's "Rochester region" of New York State. This region, comprised of eleven counties, with 1.3 million people, is conforming to the state air classification plan and standards. Monroe County has even adopted a pollution code of its own. Almost all of the four hundred industries in the region are already complying with stringent state air quality standards or have submitted schedules for compliance by next year when the standards go into effect officially. Almost all incinerators in the eleven counties now meet state standards and almost all remaining open dumps are making progress toward complying with state rules against pollution of the atmosphere.

It might be said that Rochester has a tradition of clean industries and civic pride, that its all-but-unanimous record of compliance is not typical. But consider the huge industrial complex around Buffalo, New York, which also has its civic pride—even though its pollution problems were so serious that *Fortune* magazine once took "how-not-to-do-it" environmental pictures of the region from the air.

Buffalo today is no longer a forest of smokestacks pouring filth into the skies. How this happened on the Niagara frontier is a virtual case history of the drive to eradicate air pollution as a menace to public health.

Under the State Air Pollution Control Program, these companies in Niagara County converted almost at once from coal to clean-burning gas installation: Varcum Chemical, Electric City Paper Company, Buffalo Forge, Upson Company, and the Whitnor Chemical Company. Modifications of the boiler system at the National Paper Company cut smoke emission to an acceptable level. Carborundum

Company, pending the changeover, is using a better grade of coal for cleaner and more efficient operation, and is installing control devices on many of its furnaces.

The Hooker Company of Niagara Falls shut down one of its boilers because of its continuous smoke emission, eliminated chlorine emissions by the installation of a scrubber, and corrected black smoke emissions from a chemical residue burner. International Paper Company is developing a packed tower scrubber that will completely eliminate its odor problems near Niagara Falls.

Niagara County completed its incinerator investigation schedule in June 1969, and has since eliminated 113 out of 276 incinerators. Twenty-eight out of 33 industrial and commercial incinerators were approved, as were 80 out of 105 home incinerators. A new solid waste agency was created in the county, and all thirteen of the town and municipal open-burning sites have been shut down. There are two county and five municipal sanitary landfill sites in operation around Buffalo in a very long step ahead toward clean solid waste disposal.

In Erie County, Bethlehem Steel Company's Lackawanna plant, often singled out as a major source of pollution, has complied with state orders for improvements. In July 1968 ducting to allow the cleaning of all the effluent from its Open Hearth Shop No. 2 was completed. In October 1968 fume and dust collection systems were put into operation and open burning was discontinued in the installation. In the fall of 1969 hoods were constructed above polluting industrial processes, and draft fans were added. Open Hearth Shop No. 3 was brought into compliance in December 1969, after two particularly troublesome furnaces were shut down.

Republic Steel Corporation, whose major pollution sources were identified by the state as open hearth furnaces, will take them out of service when a new basic oxygen furnace is completed later in 1970. The Amherst Foundry voluntarily committed itself to the purchase of expensive scrubbing equipment for the cupola of the foundry, and is well within state air quality standards. Trico Products converted all coal-operated boilers to oil, and Worthington Corporation ended the burning of coal in its powerhouse.

Westinghouse Electric Company's new facilities in Erie County use clean-burning natural gas and all of Ashland Oil Refinery's powerhouse boilers use oil. Ashland is constructing a new desulfurizing unit which will remove sulfur from the fuel oil consumed on the plant site. Pohlman Foundry has installed new electric induction furnaces for smelting metal and is reducing its emissions significantly across the board.

The City of Buffalo itself is keeping pace with private industry. The city opened a new 250-ton-per-day refuse incinerator in October 1969 and is installing the newest air pollution control devices on all remaining older incinerators.

These great gains have already made a visible difference in an area of our state that was once seriously affected by atmospheric pollution. As one of our citizens said, "If Buffalo can make it, so can anybody." And this is an example of what I mean—in real life, not just theory—when I say we *can* save our environment.

THREE

Noise: The Quiet Issue

We have made progress in cleaning up the atmosphere, in part, because the public recognizes the health dangers and is willing to accept the expenditures. But there has been little progress, nationally speaking, against noise pollution, because so little is known about the subject.

Yet the Surgeon General of the United States said not long ago that between six million and sixteen million Americans were going deaf right now from occupational noise. This statistic is shocking. It also is typical of our basic lack of precise information in the field—for a difference of ten million people in an estimate of this nature is quite a difference.

Dr. Vern O. Knudsen, a founder of the Acoustical Society of America, has said that, "Noise is a slow agent of death." Noise pollution is, in fact, a threat to millions that could be as dangerous as the pollution of the atmosphere. Clinicians believe that prolonged exposure to noise, especially to sharp, sudden, surprise sounds, produces severe involuntary responses in the digestive, vascular, and nervous systems. Dr. Samuel Rosen, Clinical Professor of Otology at

Mount Sinai School of Medicine in New York City, recently described this process:

"Epinephrine is shot into the blood as during stress or anxiety. The heart beats rapidly, the blood vessels constrict, the pupils dilate, the heart turns, the skin pales, and the stomach, esophagus, and intestines are seized by spasms. When the noise is prolonged, there are heart flutters that eventually subside when the noise diminishes."

Medical World News recently reported the results of an important three-year study of university students conducted by the Max Planck Institute in West Germany. The fairly constant application of sound levels of 70 decibels consistently caused vascular constriction. This would be particularly dangerous if coronary arteries were already narrowed by atherosclerosis. In animal experiments, in the United States, rabbits subjected to eight weeks of high noise showed elevated cholesterol levels and atherosclerosis, but there was still insufficient information to show a similar direct effect in humans.

Human ears cannot shut out noise in sleep in the same way eyelids shut out light. The constriction of blood vessels by noise pollution can go on all night long. Many people, fast asleep, are fatigued by their efforts to remain asleep in the midst of urban noise. One of the most effective posters of the National Environment Teach-in, in my opinion, showed elephants wandering happily about, their mighty ear flaps protecting them from environmental noise, beaming at humans who have no ear flaps.

The United States Public Health Service said in 1970 there was no doubt whatever that environmental noise caused serious hearing defects. Construction workers who operate jackhammers and airport employees who do not wear ear protectors were specifically running the risk of deafness. The Public Health Service said men and women who worked anywhere near bulldozers, scraper loaders, compactors, and earth-moving equipment, or anywhere near airport ramp areas, or in such noisy manufacturing plants as paper bag factories, would probably sustain some loss of hearing.

Dr. Rosen measured the hearing of the Mabaan tribe in the quiet southern Sudan, in Africa, and of the Lapps in northern Finland, to support his insistence that noise pollution was dangerous, not merely the latest episode of an environmental hue and cry. He found that Mabaans, who benefited from fat-free diets and freedom from high blood pressure as well as peace and quiet, heard a great deal better than westerners. Then came his clincher: Mabaans in their seventies heard as well as Mabaans in their teens—and suffered no loss of hearing in their whole lives. His findings were generally confirmed among the Lapps.

The lowest audible sound is one decibel—and louder sounds are measured upward on a logarithmic scale. Twenty decibels is ten times 10 decibels, and 80 decibels is a million times louder than 20 decibels. A dropped pin is six or so decibels—and 30 or so if it is dropped on a parquet library floor. The ordinary conversation level in an average-size room runs at approximately 60 decibels. Sounds of 80 decibels or more are uncomfortable to human ears. Decibel levels of 90 or more are estimated by otologists to present a health hazard. Decibel levels of 100 or more are a definite threat to hearing.

Heavy city traffic in 1970 is measured at 90 to 95 decibels, and a common household food blender at 93 decibels. Pneumatic hammers and air compressors along city sidewalks erupt in sudden blasts of 95 decibels or more. Power mowers on suburban lawns roar as monstrously as urban traffic, with readings in excess of 95 decibels. This is also the reading, incidentally, of a subway train screaming around a curve. Farm tractors can clock 98 decibels, roughly the same as a newspaper printing press.

Incredible as it may seem, there are many familiar implements of modern life that measure 100 decibels and above. These include loud outboard motors, powering along offshore, 102 decibels; textile looms, 106 decibels; riveting guns, 110 decibels on up, usually way up.

"The acoustic trauma of rock music is insidious," said Dr. Frederick L. Dey, at the conclusion of a noise pollution study he conducted for the National Institute of Neurological Diseases and Blindness. He said two hours' exposure to 110-decibel rock would cause "an usually severe temporary audiometric threshold shift in about 16 per cent of young men exposed." He meant that some three out of twenty would suffer hearing damage.

As for the musicians, an audiologist on Dr. Dey's survey said, "It's simple. It's common for them to wear ear plugs. They've learned how damaging the music can be."

Then there are the psychological effects of noise pollution. "Nobody has any answers about this yet, but we need them, very badly," said a spokesman for the National Institute of Mental Health. It is likely that startling sounds contribute to outbursts of anger among normally placid people. A dropped toy, a blaring television set, a police siren, a tingling telephone, a sudden truck noise, might propel a neurotic to minor violence. As for prolonged, steady sound, men and women exposed to it are more inclined to quarrel or act irrationally.

A British study showed not long ago that people who lived near deafening London Airport were admitted to mental hospitals at a higher rate than people living in quiet districts in the same part of the country.

"The noises of our daily life have been blamed variously for the high divorce rate, social conflict, indigestion, nervous breakdown, high blood pressure, heart failure, and even insanity," said Dr. Leo L. Beranek, one of the United States' foremost acoustical authorities. Dr. Beranek believes that most of these suggestions resulted from undue imagination, "but one cannot rule out the possibility that some people are particularly sensitive to noise, just as others are to nuts, eggs, or dust."

The damage is done deep in the inner ear, near the brain, to the delicate cilia, rows of microscopic, hairlike organs capable of responding individually to thousands of frequencies of sound. The first of these tiny organs to be injured by noise are those which respond to the higher frequencies, above the level of speech. But the hearing loss takes place very gradually, and deafness is often not noticed until it is too late to take corrective measures.

The New York State Labor Department's Division of Industrial Hygiene, which has been setting noise standards in industry for years, is conducting a survey at the invitation of the National Knitted Outerwear Association, a federation of manufacturers, distributors, and contractors with offices in Manhattan. The knitted outerwear industry is a significant one in New York State. Almost six out of ten of the industry's American mills are located there. The association is anxious to discover the extent of the industry's compliance with noise limits, and to help safeguard the hearing of the employees.

"The special danger of industrial noise," says Dr. Philip M. Bourland of the Industrial Hygiene Division, "lies in the fact that a man is exposed day after day to the same frequencies and high sound levels. This is what can cause occupational hearing loss and what makes it different from deafness caused by an acute injury such as an explosion."

In a recent state inspection of one association mill, a hand air gun used to blow lint off a stationary machine registered a sound level of 90 to 91 decibels at the ear of the workman using it. This was approximately as loud as a subway train.

In another room at the mill, equipped with long tables for cutting the knitted material, an "up-and-down cutter," a motorized knife which sliced through several plys of knitted material, registered a sound level of 75 to 76 decibels, about the level of noise produced by an average automobile passing at a distance of thirty feet. Some "up-and-down cutters" in similar operations produced noise levels as high as 91 decibels, comparable to the noise levels produced by household blenders. "But in cases such as this, the noise is definitely louder to the operator than it is to you or me," explained an engineer. "He's got to get close to his work—and close to the noise."

A steady, loud noise enveloped the inspection team at a "brushing" machine, into which a workman was feeding a wide piece of knitted material for sweaters. The machine roughed up the surface of the material on a rotating drum covered with hundreds of steel needles. The main source of sound was a vacuum device which drew away the loose lint. Its even-toned whoosh sounded like a home vacuum cleaner—but it was much louder, 97 decibels overall.

Then state engineers discovered that one circular knitting machine was noisier than others. They positioned noise-measuring instruments around the machine to determine the exact source of the extra noise. This proved to be a loose belt and pulley.

"The popular idea of a noisy factory is a 'boiler works,'" said Dr. Morris Kleinfeld, director of the Division of Industrial Hygiene. "But there are others such as knitting mills which are less obvious but are prime candidates for study. Newspaper pressrooms, for example, are using new presses which are faster and consequently noisier. Metal-forming and processing plants, such as foundries, are others that may require study.

Following the field surveys, said Dr. Kleinfeld, the state would make audiometric surveys, or hearing tests, in industries where the investigations disclosed the presence of

dangerous sound levels. "Our ultimate aim," said Dr. Kleinfeld, "is a flexible and workable industrial code rule for the
regulation of noise, one which can meet the varying noise
problems of industry in New York State."

In New York City, more personal, subjective terms were
often used by men and women in their correspondence to
Mayor Lindsay's Task Force on Noise Control. For
example:

Unbearable,
Agonizing,
Nightmarish,
Unendurable.

Letters from residents said, "It is impossible to spend a
quiet evening at home," "family living, because of the motorcycle noise, is virtually nightmarish," "the pernicious and all
persuasive pneumatic drills provide me with a rude and
jarring awakening," "the people in our showroom complain bitterly—you can hardly hear anyone talk." The
Mayor's Task Force reported "a feeling of frustration, con-
strained rage, and anxiety" about noise pollution, and it
asked: "Should a few, apart from the indigenous worth of
their activities, be permitted to disturb the lives of many?"

The Task Force, led by Neil H. Anderson, executive vice-
president of the New York Board of Trade, recommended
that noises interfering with the normal level of human
speech should be reduced as soon as possible. There should
be lower levels for wholly residential areas, 40 decibels by
day and 30 by night. The Mayor's then-administrator for
environmental protection, Dr. Merrill Eisenbud, said it
would take "a decade or more for a meaningful reduction
in noise."

In fact, most city dwellers have "invented" their own
method of combatting noise pollution. They turn on a low-
decibel producer—a fan or an air conditioner—to strain out
and distill the louder noises and make them more palatable.

The First National City Bank in New York City thought of a solution for the problem of high employee turnover in one of its clattering check-processing departments. The bank hired qualified clerical help from among the ranks of the deaf. The bank now has some three hundred deaf employees. The experiment was a tremendous success, and it is being extended. Meanwhile, the noise goes on.

In addition to enforcing the general law for the abatement of nuisances, New York State has moved specifically in recent years against noise pollution on the highways. We passed laws against defective motorcycle mufflers, against sirens and gongs on other than emergency vehicles, against inadequate mufflers on automobiles. Then we moved against "excessive or unusual noise of motor vehicles." We set the noise limit at 88 decibels at speeds of less than 35 m.p.h. and 50 feet from the center of the traffic lane.

On the Thomas E. Dewey Thruway, our state troopers are measuring the sounds of trucks at varying speeds and issuing summonses to violators. CBS Laboratories in Connecticut has developed a new electronic system by which we can simultaneously measure the decibel level and photograph any car or truck emitting more than an authorized decibel level. The photograph provides impressive evidence in court.

New York City prohibits the use of automobile horns on stationary vehicles, except as a danger signal, and on moving vehicles only as a danger signal. The city also bans the use of any vehicle so loaded, so "out of repair," as to create loud and unnecessary grating, rattling, or other noise. The city forbids the unnecessary blowing of steam whistles and, along with the state, the use of a stationary internal combustion engine without an effective muffler. There are city laws against excessive noise near schools and hospitals and in the loading and unloading of vehicles. The shouting of street peddlers is forbidden.

WE "CAN" CONTROL NOISE

I believe we can control noise pollution, and we can do it now, once the general public recognizes that the problem is serious and decides to spend the necessary money. The technology is available, even if at high cost. The Ingersoll-Rand Company recently demonstrated two of its models of air compressor equipment; "the noisy one," in general use everywhere in the United States, cost between $28,000 and $30,000, while a muffled version cost $45,000.

William L. Wearly, chairman of the board of Ingersoll-Rand, said the company sold almost no quiet compressors: "Not a drop in the bucket," he said, and he did not think anybody would voluntarily switch to the more expensive models. "I think it will have to be done with regulation."

One of the principal infringements on the quality of life in our cities is apartment noise transmitted through thin walls. In 1969 New York City began to require that no more than 45 decibels of sound be conveyable through the walls of new apartments. But builders and architects said this and other noise control techniques could increase the cost of new apartment construction from 5 to 10 per cent, and asked whether the public was ready to accept this. The Task Force suggested, none too hopefully, that "noise ratings" be obtained for all new apartments, and for older ones that become vacant. This would be a consumer protection device enabling prospective tenants to know, before signing a lease, what noise conditions they could expect.

Meanwhile, the dull hum of fans and air conditioners continues to be the citizen's principal weapon against neighbors' conversations. One Manhattan firm offers a new household machine, selling for $20, that sounds like a tuneless Muzak even though it is advertised as the sound of the wind in the pines. Once, a Manhattan hotel relayed the noises of cows mooing and crickets cricketing into guest rooms, but the promotional practice has been discontinued.

The development of off-site, prefabricated housing under the current leadership of the Office of Housing and Urban Development in Washington offers new hope of effective noise controls. It is simpler and less costly to install these controls as the new materials come off the assembly line. Another promising new concept is the development of portable, soundproofed rooms for installation in homes, offices, or industrial plants.

Noise control technology in transportation is also available right now. General Motors has designed quieter sanitation trucks, conducting new research into noise abatement features of body and chassis design, and making its findings available to other manufacturers. Having produced the engine and chassis for a sanitation truck estimated to be 60 per cent quieter than the usual clattering variety, GM won a contract for eleven hundred of them to be introduced into New York City within the next two years. Each quiet garbage truck costs about $100 more than a noisy one.

On a national level, there is infinite opportunity right now for an all-out campaign against truck noise, similar to the one we are waging in New York State. This is *the* problem of highway noise pollution. On the Connecticut Turnpike, with a commercial traffic of more than 16 per cent, one in ten of the passing vehicles violates the 88-decibel limit and rates up to 94 decibels or more. But on the Merritt Parkway in Connecticut, where trucks are prohibited, engineers have discovered after 2500 test measurements that not a single vehicle violates noise control standards. In this area of environmental protection, the automobile is not guilty.

Trucks may be required to reduce diesel engine noise by simple techniques that have already been tested in diesel bus design, basically a sealed engine compartment, mechanically ventilated by fans. Air brake noise, that frantic pumping sound, may be reduced by small discharge and line mufflers. Tires may be designed with cross bar and rib treads to minimize the familiar whirring noise.

THE AVIATION NOISE PROBLEM

The air transportation industry also has a major noise problem. New York State Attorney-General Lefkowitz recently brought suit against fifty-eight domestic and foreign airlines and the Port of New York Authority to compel reduction of noise levels in airport neighborhoods. "The airlines claim they may be able to reduce noise by 1974," the attorney-general said. "Well, I want them to move sooner . . ."

Late in 1969 John H. Shaffer, chief of the FAA, proclaimed a new set of federal noise level standards designed to halve the racket of jet landings and takeoffs. The new regulation applied to large new jet aircraft, but the Boeing 747 was exempted from the new noise rule until December 1971. This meant that 170 of the 193 747s on order would not be covered by the new antinoise standards. The even newer Lockheed 1011s and the DC-10s would be covered, and this would be a long step forward. But Mr. Shaffer told a delegation of United States congressmen from airport communities around the nation that he would not require Boeing to make the 747 quieter before putting it into production.

"There are 235,000 people employed in the 747 program," he said. "Should I put my foot down and put those people out of work so as to meet a noise standard?" Presumably, the question answers itself—but it also emphasizes the constant dilemma of choice between economic and environmental priorities.

The 747s are actually quieter than the smaller Boeing 707s and Douglas DC-8s, the workhorse jet transports of the

1960s. But now the airlines are considering the extension of the lives of the workhorses by ten to fifteen years or more by installing new wing assemblies at a cost of $300,000 or more per aircraft. The old jets are that good—but how to handle the noise problem? A retrofit of the hundreds of jets across the world would cost literally billions of dollars, according to the FAA, and it would take at least four years.

The technology is available, in one field of airport noise control, at reasonable cost. The noise of run-up testing of aircraft engines on the ground may be reduced dramatically by suppressors. These are cylinders or boxes placed behind the aircraft engines to diffuse exhaust gases and minimize sounds. There are also available some reflective walls and baffles and portable screens which absorb the roar of the jets in test.

"Transportation noise is a form of environmental deterioration of major concern to this administration," says U. S. Transportation Secretary John A. Volpe. One priority would seem to be the installation of muffling equipment on all 747s and eventually all 707s and DC-8s. Beyond this, we will face a wholly new commercial aviation problem later in this decade when supersonic transports—British-French, Russian, or American—start spanning the globe with their sonic booms.

Aircraft technology is only one part of the problem, however. The other is the quality of life in residential, industrial, and wildlife areas in the vicinity of airports. In Florida, conservationists recently succeeded in detouring, then derailing a project for a large jetport in the Everglades. In the New York-New Jersey area, the search for a badly needed fourth jetport has been delayed for years by the public uproar over the noises that such a jetport would bring to the community selected as the site.

The noise of the jets is indeed substantial. But the other side of the issue is that air passenger traffic increased by only 1.2 per cent in New York in 1969 as against a nationwide growth of 8.9 per cent. This is a direct result of the overcrowding at the three major jetports of the metropolitan area—in the air and on the ground. We must relieve this overcrowding, for we can no more turn our backs upon jet transportation than upon the telephone, the electric light, or the automobile.

The Port of New York Authority is now considering a new approach. It is weighing the extension of Kennedy Airport into Jamaica Bay. This extension of airports into offshore waters is also currently under study in Chicago, Los Angeles, New Orleans, and Boston. Great Britain, which has encountered similar citizen resistance to construction of a new jetport to the north of London, is considering a fantastic plan for the building of a whole new floating airport community at Foulness, on the Thames Estuary.

The New York plan envisages the early construction of two more runways at Kennedy on landfill in nearby sections of Jamaica Bay. This would increase air traffic by some 40 per cent. There are longer-term projects for the extension of the airport along a huge runway to a new complex, to be constructed five to seven miles out in the Atlantic Ocean. The water depths along the Continental Shelf in the project areas are eighty feet or less. The new projects would be useful in terms of land reclamation and landfill, solid waste disposal, small land acquisition cost, minimum community disruption, and access to existing terminal and maintenance facilities. The principal merit is to remove much of the current noise pollution from residential communities—an alternative to soundproofing all homes near airports, for example, or condemnation of land around airports in which jet noise constitutes a health hazard.

But in ecology, no one move can be considered alone. The drawback of offshore airport construction near New York City and other major metropolitan centers is that it would damage the marine environment. Here is the issue that governed the Everglades controversy in Florida. So the Port Authority wisely commissioned the National Academy of Sciences to conduct a four-month ecological survey of Jamaica Bay. This is the first time to my knowledge that economic and ecological factors are being weighed side by side in a project of this size and type. The ecological answers might be predictable—in terms of disruptions of tidal currents and marine life. But the result could also be the development of a complete "package plan" for Jamaica Bay that would include bird refuges and other conservation measures in addition to the new jet facilities the city must have.

Environmental factors must be considered well in advance in all aspects of aviation planning. There must never again be the breakdown in communication, as seen in the Everglades dispute, in which one real estate developer said disgustedly, "Who cares about the birds? We believe in people." Obviously, we need to care about both.

The whole nature of our planet—and of the air about it, not to mention the urban regions in which 75 per cent of our people live—is conditioned by the intimate relationship of all living things.

Noise pollution is the quiet, "sleeper" issue of the environmental crisis. But when our people are fully aware of the damage done, peace and quiet surely will rank along with clean skies and pure waters as top priorities for our generation.

FOUR

Pure Waters

*"We congratulate you on being the first
governor of any state in the history of the
United States to prepare a realistic attack
upon the problem of water pollution . . ."*
National Audubon Society to
Nelson A. Rockefeller,
January 1965

Nineteen sixty-five was the year in which New York State's
pioneering Pure Waters program was inaugurated—a $1.7
billion program, first in the nation, first in the world, still
the largest of its kind on earth.

Pure Waters was a start toward reducing the pollution of
our rivers, lakes, streams, and offshore waters, a start toward reversing generations of neglect. It dramatized the
magnitude of the problem—in New York State and across
the nation. And it proved that a well-informed public
would support an effectively organized effort to wipe out
water pollution, however large the undertaking.

Both Houses of the New York State Legislature approved

Pure Waters—unanimously. The voters of the state then approved a $1 billion Pure Waters bond issue by a four to one margin. On no other single issue in my public life have I been so warmly supported by the voters. Scores of private organizations began to adopt resolutions of commendation of Pure Waters. County boards of supervisors, boards of village trustees, city councils, town boards, and local planning agencies indicated their endorsement. It was clear that almost all New Yorkers—farmers, housewives, workers, conservationists, sportsmen, businessmen, children—were ready for leadership and prompt action against water pollution. The depth of response by the people amounted to a resounding endorsement of our program.

As a result, we have made visible and encouraging progress. We helped build, and we are now operating, 143 new sewage disposal projects in New York State. We are building another 68 sewage plants. An additional 152 facilities are in various preconstruction phases. We are committed to sewage plant construction that will improve the quality of ten billion gallons of water a day—some 20 per cent of all of our fresh water resources.

Under the Pure Waters program, the state pays 30 per cent of the cost of building new sewage plants and other facilities. The state also prefinances the federal share—an additional 30 per cent. This leaves 40 per cent of the costs to be borne by the localities which, not many years ago, had to bear the whole cost or dump raw sewage into nearby waters. All too often, they did the latter.

Thus the State of New York moved dramatically to make a war on water pollution financially possible—not just a matter of tough rhetoric or unenforceable laws.

But when we looked forward in 1965 to having the whole job done by 1972, we were too optimistic. To start with, there has been a dramatic increase in sewage plant construction costs. Originally, we estimated that construction expenses would escalate by 5 per cent per year. Instead, we have experienced cost inflation of 8 to 14 per cent per year.

Then there has been the enormous shortfall in the federal effort, as noted. The federal government is currently advancing only 7 per cent of Pure Waters project expenditures—so the state is putting up most of the federal share. We hope to collect eventually—but the Congresses of the last five years (1965–70) have consistently fallen far short of actually appropriating funds to back up the promises of the Clean Waters Act, which authorizes federal grants up to 55 per cent. Such "authorizations" are meaningless when not backed by hard cash.

There are other important factors. More industries than expected are choosing to participate in shared municipal projects, with state aid, rather than build their own facilities, with tax concessions. The addition of tertiary treatment of sewage, to reduce the phosphate problem, is another costly new development. And we decided to extend the projected life of our new sewage plants to twenty-five to fifty years in order to service anticipated new increases in the urban and suburban populations. This also has added to the costs.

Early in 1970 I went to the legislature with a request for $750 million more for prefinancing the federal share of Pure Waters. This was readily approved. The total costs of Pure Waters in New York State including the private effort of up to $1 billion may now be expected, realistically, to total $4 billion. And although we have been told that much more money will be coming from the federal government, we have learned, frankly, not to count on it until we get it.

We have also learned, unfortunately, that New York State's efforts, while leading the nation in water pollution control, are all too often held back by our neighbors. For example, more than 60 per cent of the pollution of Lake Erie, on our western shores, emanates from Detroit. And nobody will be able to swim safely in the lower Hudson River Valley again until the State of New Jersey does more to clean up the Passaic River, where most of the sewage plants date back to 1924 and before. The Passaic dumps its effluence into New York Harbor. The tides sweep the mess back up the Hudson for more than fifty miles.

Despite discouragements, our pioneering effort has been well worth while. It has proved that we are on the right track, and I intend to continue it without interruption until all our waters are pure and sparkling. The problems are immense, but they need not overwhelm us. Pollution of the rivers, streams, and lakes of the United States must be ended as quickly as possible—as a prerequisite for our good future and our good health. We *can* stop water pollution if we are prepared to pay the price. The people of New York are showing how the nation can accomplish this.

BACKGROUND OF THE NEW YORK STATE EFFORT

New York State is blessed with a plentiful supply of water, enough to meet present needs and those of the predictable future. We have 3,500,000 acres of lakes and ponds, 70,000 miles of rivers and streams, and hundreds of miles of shoreline. In a normal year, we receive forty inches of rainfall. By the early 1960s, however, the pollution of these waters had become intolerable. Pollution degraded public water supplies, damaged water for industry, jeopardized health, reduced property values, wrecked commercial fishing and shellfish harvesting, ran down recreational areas used for bathing, boating, and fishing, generally defiled our environment, and exacted a high cost in aesthetic values.

In 1960, thirty-two hundred people in a small town south of Albany were stricken with shigella dysentery spread from a drinking water supply. Four hundred cases of hepatitis were identified among people who ate clams from polluted

Raritan Bay in New Jersey. In 1965 an outbreak of encephalitis infected ninety-four people and caused eight deaths in New Jersey; it was traced to polluted waters in which mosquitoes bred. When some children ate a watermelon they had fished from New York Harbor, they contracted typhoid fever.

The basic technology of sewage control is well established. The primary need is for more sewage treatment plants and interceptors. Municipal collection systems gather the wastes in lateral and trunk sewers. When treatment is not provided, the wastes are dumped directly into the nearest waters. Interceptors are designed to gather wastes from these trunk and lateral sewers and bring them to the treatment facilities. Interceptors have to be provided where existing collection systems have multiple sewer outlets discharging directly into watercourses.

Treatment plants receive wastes from collection systems and from interceptors. Treatment will then eliminate many of the harmful properties of wastes by sedimentation, biological or chemical action, and disinfection. Primary treatment (sedimentation) is always necessary. Secondary treatment (biological and chemical action) is almost always necessary. Chlorination (disinfection) is needed in most cases.

To eliminate existing pollution in industries not tied in to municipal waste systems, there must be separate industrial facilities and even changes in industrial processes.

In the early days of the Pure Waters program, it soon became apparent that regional plants covering several communities would be more efficient and more economical than a large number of smaller plants. We therefore conducted scores of comprehensive sewerage studies embracing whole counties or parts of counties. The state paid some $5 million for these studies—and the local governments gained experience holding referenda, educating the public, and financing the local share of new construction, often in spite of difficult financial circumstances. Once the legal and financial arrangements were made, the communities obtained even more detailed engineering reports. They submitted these to the state along with their requests for funds.

The value of the comprehensive studies, which took time, and the public support, which often was ahead of us, soon paid off in the results of referenda. In Livingston County, 68 per cent of the eligible voters in the Conesus Lake Sewer District turned out to approve a $6.4 million project by more than three to one. This was the first known attempt to sewer a lakefront completely. A referendum in the South Chautauqua Lake Sewer District approved $7 million for consolidation of waste-water facilities and protection of the lake after the local health department guided a public information campaign. A huge $269 million referendum for sewerage in suburban Suffolk County on Long Island was approved by a large majority in November 1969.

In Monroe County and the city of Rochester, Pure Waters moved ahead on a textbook schedule—and an account of this progress affords some glimpses of the complexities. A $550,000 state grant from the State Department of Health, authorized as early as 1964, funded basic engineering studies covering the entire 673 square miles of Monroe County. By 1967 the Monroe County Legislature created a "Pure Waters Agency" which drafted a countywide water quality management plan and outlined its implementation. Two pure water districts were quickly created, and the county proceeded toward the construction stage in both. Contracts were awarded after competitive bidding for a vast amount of pipe, needed for the network of interceptor sewers which would clean up local streams, the Genesee River, and the Lake Ontario shore. Plans were drafted for bidding for a new treatment plant which would receive waste waters from the northwest area of the county. This plant would have a one-mile-long outfall tunnel extending into Lake Ontario.

The city of Rochester developed a plan for upgrading its own sewage treatment plant with an 18,000-foot-outfall. This plant would receive sewage from the east side of the county. A third major treatment plant serving the southwest area was upgraded and that work was prepared for bidding. All of these plants in and around Rochester were designed to provide high level secondary treatment plus phosphate removal. They will be among the most advanced in the United States—and the total cost of the work will be in the neighborhood of $120 million.

Our Pure Waters program offered industry the incentive, from the start, to build its own treatment plants and receive tax benefits. Tax relief included the right to take net operating loss deductions in the year of the sewage expenditure, and to exempt treatment facilities from property taxes and special levies. Industries that opted to build their own plants submitted engineering plans to the Department of Health for review and approval. They were granted tax exemption certificates upon inspection of the completed facilities.

The state government also encouraged industries to cooperate with municipalities in joint treatment projects, pointing out the cost reductions that might result. The idea was for industries to share in new municipal-industrial waste treatment facilities and pay an annual use fee to the sewage district.

The majority of New York State business enterprises cooperated with Pure Waters. By 1969 more than sixty new industrial treatment plants were in operation, and 198 had reached the design stage. The food-processing industry ran up an outstanding record. Eight new treatment plants, including a project shared with local government, were installed in food plants. These soon began to handle wastes equivalent to those of the combined populations of the cities of Buffalo and Rochester.

But the pulp and paper industry, with more than its share of aged plants, lagged behind the pace. New York has twice as many pulp and paper mills as any other state in the country, and they contribute wastes equivalent to those of a population of two million. By the end of 1969 this industry had built or was building treatment facilities for only 15 per cent of this massive outpouring of filth.

Under the Pure Waters program, the Health Department got its first really effective weapon of enforcement. All major polluters were quickly placed on schedules for abatement of their wastes—including those of the pulp and paper industry. These were supervised under court orders, or orders from the Commissioner of Health. Whenever hard-core resistance was encountered, or major violations discovered, penalty proceedings were initiated or the cases were referred to Attorney-General Lefkowitz for court action leading as often as not to stiff fines. To mid-1970, twenty-eight penalty assessments had been initiated, and twenty-five cases sent to the attorney-general.

The Health Department also moved to control new sources of water pollution. It issued permits for discharges into state waters only after investigating the nature of the proposed effluents and the potential effect on water quality. In 1969 the Department instituted the registration of *all* waste outlets in New York State. This is quite an undertaking.

As to the institutions run by our own New York State government, when Pure Waters started it was embarrassing to find that only ten out of 152 state institutions met our own water quality standards. By the end of 1969, however, 111 state institutions (and 33 federal installations in New York) were abating their wastes satisfactorily. Thirty-one others needed additional facilities at a total estimated cost of $4.4 million; these are being provided.

We also appropriate funds in New York State to pay localities one third of the cost of operating and maintaining municipal sewage plants that meet our Health Department standards. More than sixty municipal plants now receive these grants, totaling more than $4 million in 1969.

In addition to its other benefits, the Pure Waters program is so large that it has a direct and favorable effect on the overall economy of the state. In an attempt to evaluate the impact, the State Office of Planning Coordination conducted an economic analysis of the Pure Waters program in five counties in central New York. The analysis was limited to the secondary, spinoff, indirect economic activity that would be generated around the Pure Waters program. We learned that the state might expect to gain $1.23 in terms of increased economic activity for every $1 spent in Pure Waters project costs—not to mention the many thousands of construction jobs.

PURE WATERS AUTHORITY

Since many municipalities lacked sufficient technical and financial resources to respond to the Pure Waters challenge, no matter how willing they might be, we created the State Pure Waters Authority in 1967. The Authority was given the power to undertake planning, financing, construction, maintenance, and operation of sewage treatment works and solid waste disposal facilities for municipalities—and it was a smash hit. Within three years the Authority had entered into contractual relationships with municipalities in an amount totaling more than $100 million.

The village of Westport, New York, has virtually changed its whole way of life in cooperation with the Pure Waters Authority. The village sits, a scene on a picture postcard, between the rugged Adirondacks and Lake Champlain, about sixty miles south of the Canadian border. The abundance of pike and bass in Northwest Bay and the spectacular view of the Green Mountains of Vermont across the lake have long drawn visitors to the Westport lakeshore.

For nearly half a century, residents of Westport sent raw sewage through sewer systems into the lake and into Hammond Brook, a tributary of the lake. Three times between 1921 and 1963, taxpayer referenda rejected proposals to combine the existing sewer associations into one sanitary treatment system. In 1963 the State Water Resources Commission still classified Northwest Bay waters as suitable for drinking after chlorination. But the State Health Department said pollution was increasing—and should be stopped before it became hazardous.

In 1964 property owners in Westport were asked in a referendum to approve a $350,000 local investment, to be matched by an equal federal contribution. Again, the proposal was voted down. Citizens complained that the cost to the individual owners would be prohibitive. Two years later, the Health Department ordered the municipal beach closed.

This closure of one of the village's main tourist attractions gave the people clear warning that the pollution really was serious. Municipal officials groped for a solution—and found that the cost of sewers and treatment works had risen in two years by $220,000. In March 1968 the State Health Commissioner placed the village under order to submit plans for construction of facilities to halt pollution—and further stipulated that the work be completed by December 1970.

It was about this time that Westport turned to the State Pure Waters Authority for assistance. Mayor Onslow A. Gordon III, M.D., and Trustees Donald McIntyre and Carl Collins opened discussions with the Authority in hopes of curbing the village's pollution as economically as possible.

Their goal was to fashion a plan that recognized the community's plight: Westport's wintertime population was 725 persons, about 600 less than in the summer. About 140 year-round residents were living on fixed incomes. There was no major industry to broaden the already narrow tax base. And the village was sending about 140 children to the district's central school.

Through late 1967 and most of 1968, the Pure Waters Authority staff worked with Westport officials to devise a sound way in which to meet the village's needs. After weighing the options, the village chose to have the Authority's team of professionals in engineering, municipal law, and finance supply the total service. "These services and skills would only be available to us otherwise at a greater effort and cost," Dr. Gordon noted. At the same time, the village arranged to borrow $500,000 through the Authority to finance construction of a sewage collection system.

After the signing of the service contract in November 1968, the Pure Waters Authority took over all of the problems of planning, designing, and construction of the pollution-control facilities. The Authority retained the design engineers who had been working for the village, and became responsible for investing, on behalf of the village, the funds the Authority had borrowed to help finance the project.

In July 1969 the Authority advertised for construction bids. By September the low-bidding contractors on the treatment plant and collection-system jobs had broken ground. By January 1970, residents of Westport could see concrete evidence of their investment, as workmen closed in the treatment plant and worked through the winter. To move the $1,000,000 project along as quickly as possible, the construction crews utilized the 18-inch-thick ice of Lake Champlain to support equipment and facilitate the installation of the outfall sewer line. All signs pointed toward completion of the Westport project by September 1970.

In late February of 1970, word came from Washington that the joint Village-Authority efforts to obtain a $185,000 federal grant for lateral sewer construction had been successful. The Farmers' Home Loan Administration approved the village's application for hard cash to help finance the collection system. The net effect for the typical Westport homeowner was a prospective saving of at least $30 a year off his sewer bill.

Mr. Donald McIntyre, who succeeded Dr. Gordon as mayor of Westport, said, "The village is now in the unique position of being able to plan for and implement programs which will launch this community into the decade of the '70s. This tiny place is about to become a living testimony to what can be accomplished when the forces of state and federal governments combined are brought to bear on the solution of a problem."

In my judgment, this is what the nuts and bolts of environmental protection are all about.

The Pure Waters Authority—George A. Dudley, chairman—was established as a nonprofit corporation, receiving no direct state tax support and self-sustaining through fees charged for services rendered to a municipality. The Authority is typical of a family of state agencies of recent origin, such as the State University Construction Fund, and the State Housing Finance Agency, which do good work and might well serve as models for government in the future.

The Pure Waters Authority and similar organizations share at least three basic characteristics. They are involved in the construction of physical facilities. They have a financing capability independent of state funding processes. And their effectiveness is developed through contract processes, rather than through staff hierarchies. The Pure Waters Authority enjoys a good bond rating (AA, Standard and Poor's; provisional A, Moody's) and it anticipates a ready market for its offerings whenever they are placed for bidding. The Pure Waters Authority has, in fact, been so successful it has now been expanded into the New York State Environmental Facilities Corporation, to tie in *all* the areas of our intent to protect the environment.

In the United States as a whole, the pollution of our waters has now become so bad that every single river system in the country is in ecological trouble. With each passing second, some two million gallons of sewage and other liquid waste flow into the lakes and streams of America. More than fourteen hundred sizable communities, including the city of Memphis and parts of the city of New York, still dump untreated wastes into their waters.

Thousands of industries nationwide are still resisting pollution controls for cost and other reasons. Along a stretch of the Willamette River in Oregon, a $2.1 million federal-state local campaign against water pollution reduced spoilage by twenty thousand units as measured on a test scale over a test period. But two paper mills in the same period dumped between a half million and two million units into the river and sent the beautiful Willamette down to a new low.

The federal government advanced $7.7 million in grants to build sewage treatment facilities along a section of the Mississippi, and these reduced water pollution by 147,000 measured units. But nothing would stop eighty industrial plants along the same stretch of the river from pouring in an outrageous 2.4 million units during the measured period. The federal government said this performance was also typical of the Nashua River and Ten Mile River in Massachusetts, the Tualatin River in Oregon, the Pearl River between Louisiana and Mississippi, and the Saco River and Presque Isle stream in Maine.

Small wonder that the General Accounting Office reported that the federal government had accomplished little against water pollution since 1957, even though 9400 new projects had been constructed. The sewage of half the people of America is still inadequately treated. The quality of drinking water is now definitely endangered in many areas.

The Ohio River's water is used an estimated 3.7 times by individuals, industries, and municipalities before it reaches the Mississippi. The water usually passes through one or another form of treatment before people drink it, but this does not affect many pollutants. Not long ago, researchers analyzed the contents of a bottle dipped into the Ohio River near Cincinnati. The water was found to contain coliform organisms, from sewage; viruses, including the forms that cause poliomyelitis and hepatitis; radioactive radium 226 and strontium 90, and organic chemicals including cyanide, phenols, and pesticides including DDT, heptachlor, and toxaphene. The inorganic chemicals found in the water off Cincinnati included, in alphabetical order, ammonia, arsenic, barium, boron, cadmium, chloride, copper, fluoride, iron, lead, manganese, nitrates and nitrites, phosphorus, selenium, silver, sulfate, and zinc.

The Cuyahoga River in Cleveland caught fire in the summer of 1969, when its oil sludges and municipal wastes simply burst into flames. Two railroad trestles over the burning river were almost destroyed. The Houston Ship Canal has become an open sewer for the petrochemical and other plants along its shores. Astronaut Walter Schirra testified how he could see from space the effluents pouring out of the canal to discolor the offshore waters of the Gulf of Mexico. Most of the astronauts, who are based in Houston, are now deeply involved in their spare time in public education campaigns against pollution.

Interior Secretary Walter J. Hickel was shocked by a personal inspection of oil spills on open waters. He termed the spread of fifty square miles of oil slicks off the Louisiana coast a "disaster," and he launched a federal investigation into a fire in a cluster of twelve offshore oil wells owned by the Chevron Oil Company. After the fire was extinguished, high seas prevented the "capping" of the wells and thousands of barrels of crude oil gushed toward Louisiana's coastal wildlife refuges and oyster beds, until they were blown out to sea. Secretary Hickel said the federal government would hold the company responsible for any clean-up that might be needed—and this was an important precedent. Not long afterward, Chevron was indicted by the federal government on nine hundred counts.

Meanwhile, more than ten thousand gallons of heavy oil spilled into Tampa Bay from a Greek tanker that ran aground. This was a direct hit; damage to marine and bird life, waterfront property, beaches, seawalls, boats, and oyster beds rose into the millions of dollars. Hundreds of residents, college students, and Boy Scouts answered an Audubon Society appeal and turned out to clean up some of the mess. Humble Oil & Refining Company, which had chartered the Greek tanker, said through a spokesman that Humble would pay for all damages to private and public property.

Dramatizing his concern about what is perhaps the worst environmental case history in the United States, President Nixon flew to Chicago in the spring of 1970 to demand action against the pollution of the Great Lakes. While no person is known to have died from drinking the water of Lake Erie, or from swimming on its polluted beaches, there is a valid national question as to whether or not Lake Erie is dying. Recently, the federal government identified 360 major sources of industrial waste around the lake. Some 60 per cent of the wastes in Lake Erie originated in Detroit and another 9 per cent in Cleveland, and because the lake is quite shallow, the results have been catastrophic.

New York State borders Lake Erie at its deeper, eastern end, where the pollution is not so critical. Our Conservation Department says the lake is not dead—but there has been a very sharp deterioration in marine life. Many valuable species have disappeared, or almost disappeared, such as the whitefish—and the lake herring. Yellow perch are still quite abundant, with an approximate yield in 1969 of 35 million pounds. Until twenty years ago, such species as Atlantic salmon, lake trout, whitefish, pike, and perch amounted to 80 to 90 per cent of the total yield of Lake Erie. In 1969, perch excepted, these yielded only 5 per cent of the total catch.

In April of 1970 I directed two state departments to take steps to protect consumers from mercury contamination in fish taken from Lake Erie. The Department of Agriculture and Markets began placing all fish caught commercially in Lake Erie under seizure. The Department of Conservation advised sports fishermen not to eat fish taken from the lake. Several fish samples showed levels of mercury contamination above the .5 parts-per-million level established as "safe" by the Federal Food and Drug Administration.

In Toronto, Mr. C. H. D. Clarke, chief of the Fish and Wild Life Branch of the Great Lakes Fishery Commission, said, "The trouble is lack of oxygen at lower levels, caused by decaying plants that in turn proliferate because of phosphate and organic pollution, producing a mess anyone can see." Canada holds all of the northern bank of Lake Erie, and Canadian industry also contributes to the pollution of the lake.

How much will it cost to clean up Lake Erie? *Time* magazine recently estimated $230 million. According to many leading scientists it will not be possible to make an estimate until the dumping of sewage is stopped. But the scientists believe Lake Erie *can* be saved because it is shallow, flushes out frequently, and has many outlets. One can have an approximate idea how much this job will cost, if only because Bethlehem Steel Corporation is currently investing some $22 million to control the effluence from its plant at Lackawanna, New York, on our Lake Erie shoreline. This work will be completed in 1970—$22 million just for one plant.

And once Lake Michigan is thoroughly polluted, by contrast, it may *never* be saved. The reason is that it has few outlets and flushes infrequently. What goes into Lake Michigan will probably stay there, in one form or another.

Yet 177 lakeside municipalities are still dumping tons of sewage into Lake Michigan, stimulating the abnormal growth of algae, the ruin of the beaches, and the muddying of an extremely large body of water. More than seventy large industries pump acids, steel mill refuse, oil sludge, and pulp and paper remains into the lake, often in defiance of state and federal water pollution standards.

Illinois Attorney-General William Scott is filing two hundred suits against polluters along Lake Michigan which have violated the state environmental laws. The Federal Water Pollution Control Administration names United States Steel Corporation as the largest polluter of Lake Michigan, and the city of Milwaukee as the worst offending municipality. South Bend, Indiana, is the second worst offender. And while the city of Chicago prides itself on its longtime accomplishment in diverting its sewage away from the lake toward the Mississippi and the sea, the prospering suburbs of the North Shore pour so much filth into Lake Michigan that many of the North Shore beaches are polluted.

President Nixon's plan for the Great Lakes is, essentially, to pump sewage out of the lakes to dry land. There it would be carted off to somewhere acceptable—to "containment areas"—and left to dry out. The Army Corps of Engineers has conducted experiments in five small, diked sites around the Great Lakes and, as one officer said, "The biggest problem is cost." One estimate of the program amounts to $70 million for the thirty-five "most polluted" harbors and rivers, of which the federal government would advance a significant proportion. But Russell E. Train, the chairman of the White House Council on Environmental Quality, said the problem will not be solved until poorly treated waste materials are no longer dumped in the Great Lakes.

President Nixon also looked to the environmental protection of coastal waters. "About 48 million tons of sludge and other materials are annually dumped off the coastlands of the United States," he said. "In the New York area, alone, the amount of annual dumping would cover all of Manhattan island to a depth of one foot in two years." He wisely set in motion a federal-state study of ocean dumping to be completed in 1970. This would lead to legislation, the President said, that would avert "the same ecological damages that we have inflicted on our inland waters."

Mr. John Clark, acting director of the Sandy Hook Marine Laboratory, had a fantastic comment on offshore pollution that he documented with shocking photographs. Many fish in New Jersey waters had neither tails nor fins. This was caused not by evolution, but by pollution, and the fish looked hideous.

He added: "Bacteria live in these waters normally and are usually harmless because they are low in numbers. But when you fill up a bay with organic matter, they live in profusion and attack the fish. The fish develop fin rot, which eats away their tails and fins. They wither away. Their scales and skin tissue sluff away."

Meanwhile, in New York State in 1970, the Pure Waters program was moving along at increasing speed. Early in the summer, the state made a grant of more than $86 million to Nassau County Sewer District No. 3 to help control the pollution of the Great South Bay of Long Island and to help conserve drinking water supplies. There will be a new sewage plant, a pump station, and sewer facilities for 21 square miles of suburban land that will soon have a population of more than 200,000. Next we sent more than $84 million to the neighboring Suffolk County Southwest Sewer District for a sewage plant and sewers designed to serve 36,000 acres and a population of more than 240,000.

In the same month, the state also made a $28 million grant for the improvement of water pollution controls on the upper East River in New York City. This would help build additions to a sewage plant for 1,125,000 people, capable of handling 150 million gallons per day. Then we allocated more than $25 million to New York City for new water treatment facilities in the Harlem River and adjacent waterways. These would serve 1,150,000 city dwellers in the Bronx and would be capable of handling 200 million gallons per day.

These huge commitments were matched proportionately in smaller cities, suburbs, towns, and villages everywhere in New York State. In suburban Westchester County, for example, we approved a $25,502,180 Pure Waters construction grant for waste-water treatment facilities to help control pollution of the Hudson River. This project will involve the construction of sewage treatment works including the upgrading and expansion of an existing primary sewage treatment plant for the city of Yonkers and the villages of Tarrytown, North Tarrytown, Irvington, and the surrounding areas. It is designed for a projected population of 808,000 and will have a capacity of 93 million gallons per day.

On another front, a new state law required holding tanks on the more than fifty thousand pleasure boats in New York State waters. Boat owners protested the cost and inconvenience of the new system, but the State Health Department and the state government itself stood firm.

DETERGENTS AS POLLUTERS

Arthur Godfrey pointed up one of the new problems when he stopped his TV commercials on television for a high-intensity enzyme detergent until the company agreed to point out its ecological hazards. The detergent industry in the United States does a business of approximately $1.5 billion per year. The world market is estimated at approximately $4.5 billion. There are twenty pounds of detergents sold in the United States for every person in the country, every year. Detergents provide an estimated 40 per cent of the phosphates that contribute to water pollution nationwide. These increase the growth of algae in the rivers, the "green slime," that not only fouls the waters but emits a noxious smell—notably from the Potomac River below Washington.

In New York State, a new law effective January 1, 1971, will ban sales of any soap or detergent not plainly labeled as to phosphate content. Fortunately, technology is available for the minimizing of phosphates in wastes. This is already being used at Lake Tahoe, Nevada, among other places, where nitrogen is also removed to some extent. After the primary (sedimentation) and secondary (biological and some chemical) action against the sewage, a third process begins. Phosphates are removed with a sudden, "flash mix" of lime, followed by the settling of the resultant lime sludge into a lime mud thickener, which in turn is passed into a furnace. Nitrogen, which in sewage is mostly ammonia, is attacked in a stripping tower. Ammonia is taken out in a process that includes the jetting of air through the mess. The rest is passed through separation beds, where chemicals are intended to remove more phosphates, and on through activated carbon.

We have yet scarcely begun to handle the problems of agricultural wastes, which seep into the waters in the ecological cycle, laden as often as not with herbicides and pesticides. Nor have we begun to separate storm runoff sewage from sanitary sewage in our major cities.

In New York State we are researching problems and developing solutions we could barely anticipate. We have 116 water quality monitoring stations, twelve of them fully automatic. This system is in a sense analogous to the NASA satellite system for reporting worldwide weather and other data—and is the most sophisticated of its kind in the world.

We have research teams working on twelve major projects that are expected to be useful to us years from now.

During 1969, for example, we developed a brand-new chemical-physical treatment process designed to convert waste liquids to reusable, high-quality water. We conducted the first tests in a trailer in the suburb of New Rochelle, a humble enough beginning. Now we are applying to the federal Water Pollution Control Administration for more than $2 million in financial aid for building a multi-million-dollar demonstration facility. We will use our new process to treat domestic wastes and the outpourings of the paper mills. The new system promises to be less costly, because it reduces the treatment phases to two, while still removing most viruses and harmful bacteria.

For the years beyond the 1970s, we are preparing new "contour" profiles of two of our great rivers, the Hudson and the Mohawk, for the next generation of pollution control. We are taking measurements of the variables of the rivers to enable engineers to plan ahead for the encouragement of the best possible cycle of marine life, in the light of predicted increases in human population. The tests measure the biological oxygen demand (BOD), chlorides, nitrogen, phosphorus, algae, coliform, temperature, and, in the Hudson, salt. We are also measuring geometric, topographical, and hydrological conditions in the rivers. One reason is that water tumbling and flowing rapidly will absorb more air than stagnant water.

Aerial surveys of the Hudson are now being made from a Conservation Department jet helicopter that collects data from the river while hovering thirty feet above the surface, high enough to avoid rusting from sea spray along the tidal estuary. This is quite a sight. Our engineers carefully lower their measuring instruments, approximately the size of fat rolling pins, into the teeming life of the majestic, polluted waterway. Readings are obtained, back in the helicopter, on a James Bond-type device that resembles a tiny radio.

On a clear day the men in the Conservation Department helicopter might even see the *Clearwater,* a green-painted

76-foot sloop, square-sterned, with a 106-foot mast, and its originator, Pete Seeger, the famous folk singer. Pete Seeger and his friends sail the *Clearwater*, modeled upon a sloop of the bygone days when the Hudson was pure and clear, up and down the river to dramatize their concern for pure waters. Often the conservationists stop off at harbors along the river and give wonderful folk-song festivals. There is Pete, stomping his boots, strumming his banjo, and there are historical and craft exhibits, also slide shows put on by our own state Pure Waters Authority. Sometimes, four hundred people visit the *Clearwater* every hour, and on Sundays the attendance is greater.

My end of the job is less glamorous, less colorful—but I'm glad Pete is so active in the cause. Pure Waters are everybody's business. We need all the help we can get.

FIVE

Power for the People

The United States is in a serious power predicament. The Federal Power Commission estimates that by the year 2000 the country will need eight times more electrical power than it currently generates. And electric power is essential to the entire fabric of our culture and society. This need for power will be one of the most disturbing problems of the rest of the twentieth century. Unless we make headway in meeting the demand, brownouts will become a commonplace in the United States, much as they already are in Argentina and Brazil.

Yet this is precisely the moment in which citizens are rejecting new power plants as menaces to the environment and infringements upon the quality of life. In Chicago, for example, the United Auto Workers and Lake Michigan property owners have sought court injunctions to prevent the construction of two nuclear power plants forty miles north of the city. The state of Minnesota has defined limits on the amounts of radioactive material that may be discharged by nuclear power plants that are fifty times more severe than the safe limits set by the Atomic Energy Commission—and this measure will effectively bring new nuclear power plant construction in Minnesota to a standstill.

Southern California Edison Company was recently turned away by two towns in which it wanted to build large new power plants. The people of Victorville, on the edge of the Mojave Desert, objected to a new coal-fired generating plant so furiously that the project was shelved. "People just didn't want that thing in their backyards," the city manager explained. Then Orange County authorities would not let the utility add to its existing plant at Huntington Beach. Southern California Edison was forced to fall back upon an expansion of its nuclear plant at San Onofre, sixty miles southeast of Los Angeles.

The Los Angeles Department of Water and Power also attempted to build a power plant at embattled Victorville, and was driven off by the citizens. As an alternative, it invested more than $6 million in the construction of a new generating unit at its coal-fired Scattergood plant in the city —but the local pollution control board would not let the city department operate the new facility. Admitting that the city had gone ahead on the construction without full clearance from the pollution people, an official said, "The board always came through in the past, but it sure didn't this time."

Mr. Floyd L. Goss, the chief engineer of the Los Angeles Department of Water and Power, told the *Wall Street Journal* that the trend was devastating. "It could result in a partial blackout of the city by 1972."

The New York Times headlined an article on the power problems: UTILITIES DAMNED AT ANY LOCATION.

"ALL OF US MUST BE ENVIRONMENTALISTS"

This dilemma of power *versus* ecology is central to the paramount concern of all of us who are environmentalists. And, with the growing pressures of population and industrialization on our natural resources, all of us living in this century must be environmentalists. It is this generation that must find the ways to accommodate man's needs to the planet's resources and do so with minimum damage and disruption.

While there are some whose concerns for the environment are limited to a desire to protect themselves from adverse conditions at the expense of their neighbors, the true environmentalist is concerned about the conditions under which all society must live—and he is dedicated to resolving the implacable confrontation between our needs and our resources. A successful equilibrium can be found. To find it, however, we must press the frontiers of science and technology, and develop new methods and techniques for meeting human wants, methods which minimize the environmental costs. We have the resourcefulness and the capacity to meet this challenge.

In May of 1968 the Power Authority of the State of New York, the New York Atomic and Space Development Authority, and the major electric utility companies in New York State joined me in presenting to the legislature a program designed to meet the immediate and future electric power needs of the state in a way compatible with our concern for the environment.

The program is designed to assure the development of the electric power generating capacity necessary for the continued economic growth of the state, while at the same time serving the public need for clean air, pure water, and a safe, congenial environment in which to live and work.

Under the program, approved by the legislature, the Power Authority was authorized to:

1. Build base load nuclear generating facilities throughout its area of service;
2. Construct hydroelectric pumped storage facilities throughout its area of service;
3. Participate with the electric utilities and the Atomic and Space Development Authority in the construction

of experimental or advanced design nuclear power generating facilities.

The legislation also broadened the powers of the Atomic and Space Development Authority by authorizing it to:

1. Participate in the incorporation of features in electric utilities' nuclear power plants required by the public interest but not necessarily directly involved in the generation of power such as those relating to health, safety, aesthetics, and conservation of natural resources;

2. Designate, acquire, prepare, and make available to the Power Authority or to electric utilities sites for nuclear facilities;

3. Participate in the construction, fueling, and operation of advanced design facilities, such as a breeder reactor, with the Power Authority and the electric utilities;

4. Contract with the electric utilities or with the Power Authority in connection with fueling of nuclear facilities.

Later, in February of 1970, the Atomic and Space Development Authority appointed the chairman of the State Public Service Commission, Joseph C. Swidler, to its Nuclear Power Siting Committee. This was in support of the expanded role I have given the P.S.C. in the protection of our environment.

In May 1970 the State Power Authority ordered its contractors and engineers to proceed at top speed on the construction of its first nuclear power plant. Located on Nine Mile Point, on the shore of Lake Ontario, the new plant will generate more than 800,000 kilowatts of electric power for the people of upstate New York. It is expected to be operational by mid-1973.

The State Department of Health approved the new project, as did the Federal Atomic Energy Commission. It is the first designed to meet the new state criteria for controlling the heat of water discharged from the plant—so-called "thermal pollution." These criteria say that, in a lake such as Lake Ontario, the temperature of waters must not be increased by more than three degrees beyond a radius of 300 feet from the point of discharge at the power plant.

The State Power Authority is also constructing a "pumped storage" hydroelectric power project in Schoharie County, some forty miles southwest of Albany. This will provide 1,000,000 additional kilowatts at times of peak consumer demand and in emergencies. And, as a by-product, a beautiful state park is also being constructed on the site. The Authority already operates the Niagara and St. Lawrence hydroelectric plants with a combined capacity of 3,200,000 kilowatts.

Seven major private utility companies supply the bulk of New York State's power needs, some 17,000,000 kilowatts. Consolidated Edison Company operates a 260,000-kilowatt nuclear plant at Indian Point, in the Hudson River Valley. Niagara Mohawk Power Corporation has another nuclear plant, of 500,000-kilowatt capacity, at Nine Mile Point close by the site of the State Power Authority's new nuclear venture. The Rochester Gas and Electric Corporation maintains the Ginna nuclear plant with 420,000-kilowatt capacity.

In the early summer of 1970, however, all three of the private nuclear power plants were out of action. Con Edison had a problem in the reactor cooling system at Indian Point. Niagara Mohawk was shut down at Nine Mile Point pending an Atomic Energy Commission inspection of cracked piping. The Ginna plant reported damage to the large, low-pressure blades of its steam turbine that would take at least a month to correct. And later in the summer, a breakdown of Con Ed's 1,000,000-kilowatt "Big Allis" generator in Queens brought a power crisis to New York City—heading the statewide list of serious problems elsewhere in fossil-fuel burning and hydroelectric plants.

Mr. Swidler, as chairman of the five-man New York State Public Service Commission, called senior executives of the utility companies into urgent conference because the state's power reserves were below acceptable levels. They reviewed their reserves, their interconnections, and their ability to contribute "pool" support to one another to meet emergencies. Mr. Swidler said "blackouts" were improbable, but there might well be "brownouts." In a brownout, electrical devices continue to operate, but with less efficiency. Light bulbs gleam not quite so brightly, air conditioners lose some of their cool, and there is a reduction in the size of the pictures on television screens.

Everywhere in the state, we are striving to meet the rising demand for reliable, inexpensive electric power—for factories and homes, for offices, for hospitals and schools—and we are finding it harder and harder to keep up. In 1965 the state's electric power need was approximately 13,000,000 kilowatts. In 1990 it will be at least 48,000,000 kilowatts. In the next twelve years, it is estimated that New York State's need for electricity will double. To put this another way, we are going to need additional power equal to that now required to light up every city, power every industry, and run every household appliance in New York State.

To meet this demand, however, more efficient generation of nuclear power is essential. This means pressing ahead with the development of a breeder reactor which will make more effective use of nuclear fuel. Other difficulties must be overcome and extended controversies must be settled. Nowhere has this been more evident than in the Storm King power project in the Hudson River Valley.

In 1963 Consolidated Edison proposed to build a pump-storage hydroelectric power plant on the Hudson River near Cornwall, New York, about forty miles upstream from New York City. To operate the plant, water would be pumped at night from the river through a tunnel to a storage reservoir on Storm King Mountain. The water would be returned, through the same tunnel, turning turbines to generate electricity during periods of peak demand in metropolitan New York City.

Some idea of the size of the proposed plant might be gained from the dimensions of the tunnel opening at the base of the mountain. It was planned to be 225 feet long, 560 feet wide, and 50 feet deep. The volume of water to be withdrawn from the river during an eight-hour period would average 18,000 cubic feet per second. This might be compared to an average tidal flow in that part of the river of 100,000 cubic feet per second.

The Storm King project is an imaginative, large-scale attempt to relieve the power shortage. I had frequently criticized power companies which had insisted on locating their facilities in the midst of cities, causing atmospheric pollution, and I was glad that Con Edison wanted to move to less densely populated areas. I was also impressed by the support of the project by most of the people who lived in and around Cornwall. They would be benefited by new jobs, new local tax revenues, and a larger place in the sun as the location of an outstanding project.

But there clearly was another side to the equation. Most conservationists were adamantly against Storm King. They argued that the project would ruin scenic values, disrupt marine life, and set back the cause of enlightened conservation. My brother Laurance S. Rockefeller consistently opposed any invasion of nearby Palisades Interstate Park lands by the project—though he also understood the urgency of the need for more power.

In 1965 I attempted to resolve this controversy and find another solution. Not long afterwards, Con Edison came up with a more acceptable alternative. Their new idea was to build the power plant for the most part underground. This would remove much of the scenic objection to the new facility—although objections on account of hazards to marine life might remain.

Meanwhile, the conservationists, led by the Scenic Hudson Preservation Conference, had gone to court to force Con Edison to find alternative means of supplying power for New York City. Though Con Edison had been granted its Federal Power Commission license to construct the pump storage hydroelectric plant at Cornwall, the United States Court of Appeals set aside this license in December of 1965. The court instructed the FPC to gather a much more complete record on the environmental factors surrounding the new plant, including potential damage to marine life, and required the FPC to balance the proposed plant against all substantial alternatives.

This was a crucial finding. This was the first time in United States history in which the FPC was ordered to weigh the need for a power plant against its potential effect on the environment in comparison with an unlimited range of possible alternatives.

The FPC asked Con Edison for biological and engineering studies to demonstrate the efficiency of protective measures in the Hudson River. Con Edison funded the study. Northeastern Biologists, Inc., a firm of consultants, implemented it. A Policy Committee was formed in recognition of the controversial nature of the project, including high-level conservation administrators from New York State, New Jersey, and Connecticut, and from two federal agencies, the United States Bureau of Commercial Fisheries and the United States Bureau of Sport Fisheries and Wildlife. A Technical Committee of senior biologists was formed.

I instructed the New York State Department of Conservation to do everything possible to develop the facts of the situation, to assist in the study, and to do what it could to add to public education about the Storm King project. Mr. Albert C. Jensen, assistant director, Division of Marine and Coastal Resources, summarized the study for the people of the state.

The study began in the autumn of 1965, and continued

until the autumn of 1968. The primary purpose was to evaluate annual and seasonal changes in the distribution of fish in the Hudson River estuary. The emphasis was on determining the abundance and distribution of fish in the river, particularly in the vicinity of the proposed water intake. Special attention was given to striped bass.

The Hudson River estuary is inhabited by more than fifty species of fish, both marine and freshwater. Many of these species spawn in the river and the young spend the first critical months of their lives in the river. The striped bass is of considerable interest to both recreational and commercial fishermen in the Hudson. It was feared that eggs and larvae of the striped bass and other fish might be drawn into the pump-storage intake and killed.

The present value of sport fishery in the lower Hudson north of the George Washington Bridge, according to the U. S. Fish and Wildlife Service, is estimated to be $20 million per year. Recreational fishermen concentrate on the striped bass but also catch shad, largemouth bass, eels, sturgeon, and several other species.

Commercial fishermen, mostly using gill nets, concentrate on shad and striped bass. However, their catches also include sturgeon, alewife, blueback herring, carp, catfish, eels, white perch, and yellow perch. The commercial fishery is declining, mostly because of dwindling catches and the high cost of fishing gear.

In three years of work, the biologist determined the distribution and abundance, in time and space, of all fish life stages—from eggs, through larvae, to adults—in the section of the Hudson River that would be affected by the operation of the proposed Storm King plant. They determined the distribution and abundance of these life stages in the river above and below Cornwall. They calculated the impact of possible losses in the striped bass fisheries in the area if the plant were to be built and operated. They also collected data on the water temperature, dissolved oxygen, salinity, and other factors that made up the environment of the various life stages of the fish.

The study yielded hundreds of jars and vials containing thousands of eggs, larvae, and larger sizes of fish. These kept the teams of technicians busy for months examining the collections under the microscope, sorting and separating the species and tabulating their lengths and numbers. All of the field measurements of temperature, salinity, weather, depth of water, and the laboratory data were coded for automatic data processing. The processed data then were fed into computers for analysis. The final step required the services of trained, experienced fishery biologists to examine and evaluate the computer analyses.

The biologists found that large numbers of eggs, larvae, and young-of-the-year striped bass would be withdrawn from the Hudson River estuary by the proposed hydro-electric plant if it were to be built and operated. However, and this was most important, the eggs and young fish that would be withdrawn would be but a small percentage of the total number of each of the life stages of striped bass present in the estuary.

Whether or not the young fish in the Cornwall area might be vulnerable to passing into the intake would depend upon their size and abundance. A stainless-steel screen with a mesh size of 0.375 x 0.375 inches square placed over the mouth of the intake canal would block the passage of striped bass larger than two inches long. The stripers this size also would be able to escape from the 1.0 feet per second—slightly more than half a mile per hour—velocity of the intake current.

The results of the study also showed that substantial numbers of blueback herring, alewife, tomcod, and white perch, small enough to pass through the screens, also would be withdrawn seasonally but the effect of losses by the operation of the plant probably would be minimal. Young-of-the-year shad are found in the area of the proposed plant intake only after they have grown big enough to avoid the screens. But the bay anchovy is small enough to pass through the screens during the first two years of its life—and here the losses would be substantial.

I have drawn this much detail out of our Conservation Department report because it is typical of the real issues we have to weigh when we in government consider such emotion-charged power projects as Storm King. The report does not cover other environmental areas of contention surrounding the project and, although typical, it is not intended to be conclusive. The debate goes on, at an intense and expert level. So does the action in the courts.

Late in 1969 an examiner of the Federal Power Commission recommended once again that Con Edison be permitted to start work on the power plant at Cornwall. This would now be located for the most part underground, on the revised model that I had found much more acceptable. It seemed that the matter was close to decision. Then New York City officials asked the FPC to reverse the examiner. The new claim was that the construction of the plant itself would necessitate blasting near enough to endanger the Catskill Aqueduct water system, which brings in 40 per cent of New York City's water supply.

In May 1970 the FPC held another round of oral arguments on the New York City claim that "any avoidable risk to the water supply of eight million people is a risk that should not be taken." A decision is awaited.

Meanwhile, we learned of a sad event at the Con Edison nuclear power plant at Indian Point which resulted in a fish kill. Hudson River fish, including striped bass, white perch, herring, and sturgeon, had been sucked into a water intake. The State Conservation Department confirmed to me that the kill was "substantial." Precisely what happened is still a matter of controversy. In any event, Attorney-General Lefkowitz charged Con Edison with serious violations and asked that the Indian Point plant be closed until "suitable methods" to protect the Hudson were put into effect. He also sought $5 million in damages for the fish kills.

"The plant should not be allowed to operate until suitable methods and procedures are instituted which will enable defendant to withdraw water from and discharge water into the Hudson River in such a manner as to avoid the killing of fish and other forms of marine life and to further avoid endangering the ecology of the Hudson River," Lefkowitz said. In the final analysis, the Attorney-General's purpose was to obtain corrective measures, not to close the plant. These measures were being undertaken as this was written.

CONTROLLING THERMAL POLLUTION

It is perfectly possible to locate and design nuclear power plants with minimum hazard to the environment. The agitation against the plants has obscured the technological possibilities. In September 1969 I announced the adoption by the New York State Water Resources Commission of our new criteria for governing the "new" form of pollution, thermal pollution, the discharge of excessively heated liquids into rivers, estuaries, and lakes. These were the first thermal pollution standards to be accepted anywhere in the United States.

Thermal pollution is a problem peculiarly associated with nuclear power plants because the reactors heat the water in very large quantities. When this water is discharged back into the rivers after use, it is very damaging to marine life. Furthermore, wastes in hot water absorb oxygen more rapidly than in cool water. Thermal pollution can help create excessive growth of algae. The ecological cycle is disrupted.

In New York, therefore, we prohibited any discharge into lakes which might raise surface temperatures by more than three degrees beyond a radius of 300 feet or equivalent areas. We forbade any increase in the temperature of coastal waters of more than four degrees over the monthly high average during October through June, nor by more than 1.5 degrees during July through September beyond a radius of 300 feet or the equivalent area.

In estuaries such as the Hudson, if surface temperatures exceeded 83 degrees, an increase of no more than 1.5 degrees would be permitted between July and September. And, at any time, at least 50 per cent of the volume of the flow of the estuary, including at least one third of the surface water, must not be raised by more than four degrees, or above a maximum level of 83 degrees.

We were bombarded with demands for information on how these new thermal criteria would be applied to the nuclear power plants in the state. Con Edison is building a complex of nuclear power plants near its present facility at Indian Point. We set the criteria here at 83 degrees maximum surface temperature. The protection of the striped bass in this area, as we have seen, presents a special problem. The State Atomic and Space Development Authority is completing negotiations with Con Edison for the furnishing under lease of new facilities at Indian Point to prevent thermal pollution.

Our State Power Authority's new nuclear power plant at Nine Mile Point on Lake Ontario is well within the thermal pollution limit for lakes. Long Island Lighting Company is constructing a nuclear plant on the shores of Long Island Sound, within the criteria for coastal waters, but there is much citizen concern here about possible radiation as well as thermal pollution hazards.

Not long ago, the New York State Gas and Electric Company attempted to build an 830,000-kilowatt, nuclear-fueled electric generating plant on the eastern shore of our beautiful Lake Cayuga. But a group of Cornell University professors, aided by citizens' action groups, argued expertly that thermal pollution in a lake of this size and nature would be extremely deleterious. They were authorities in biology, icthyology, limnology, and radiology. The company put its plans in abeyance.

There are places where nuclear power plants belong, and places where they do not. There are also ways in which our advancing nuclear technology can make improvements. For example, it is possible to build cooling towers at nuclear plants, in which the heated water is cooled before being released back to the river or lake. These cooling towers are expensive, however, and 350- to 450-foot towers do not improve the scenery. It is also possible to create new lakes of great scenic and recreational value in which the pure but heated water can be cooled.

The New York State Atomic and Space Development Authority is spending much of 1970 and 1971 finding suitable sites for the construction of more nuclear power plants. For example, it is conducting aerial infrared surveys to determine the temperature characteristics of the major rivers, lakes, estuaries, and coastal waters of the state.

The survey involves the use of a "thermal mapper"—an airborne instrument which scans the surface of the ground and water below, senses the temperature-related infrared emissions and records them on a continuously unrolling photographic film that appears to produce a light-sensitive "picture" but which in fact is a recording of temperature.

The "thermal mapper" technique was developed for military purposes and has only recently become available for civilian application. Through the use of the technique, temperature variations in water, whether from natural or artificial causes, can be ascertained as well as the extent of the areas in which heat from artificial sources is dissipated under different hydrological conditions. This is an important guide to locating a power plant.

LOCATING POWER LINES

The location of power lines also has enormous environmental implications. The supporting towers are large, the lines are bulky, and, together with the cleared easement through the forests and over the hills, they materially alter the natural values of the landscape.

I have obtained legislation in New York State under which construction on any major transmission facility is prohibited unless a "certificate of environmental compatibility and public need" is obtained under a proceeding before the Public Service Commission. The bill will, for the first time, permit individuals and organizations concerned with the environment to participate in siting proceedings from the outset.

The bill creates a Temporary State Commission on the Environmental Impact of Major Public Utility Facilities to develop a procedure for resolving questions relating to power generating facilities. The commission will investigate and hold public hearings with interested persons and various public and private bodies concerned with all aspects of the siting problem.

In June of 1969 the Hudson River Valley Commission— as the state's environmental watchdog in that area—withheld its consent for a portion of a 345,000-kilowatt power line to be constructed across a scenic area of the valley.

Orange & Rockland Utilities, Inc., through its president, said the decision was "very disappointing." The line was described as one of the most vitally needed interconnections in the United States. Many major utilities were involved in the construction of a line that would connect the Pennsylvania-Maryland-New Jersey system with the New York-New England power systems. "I don't see any way of putting it underground," said the president of Orange & Rockland about his fourteen-mile section of the line. As a matter of fact, to bury a power line of that capacity might increase its cost prohibitively—by 2000 per cent.

Nonetheless, the Hudson River Valley Commission would not approve Orange & Rockland's plan to string the big line on 125-foot towers across Buckberg Mountain. It stopped work on the line with this warning:

"The benefits of the project, though substantial in terms of reducing the possibility of a power blackout, are not sufficient to justify constructing the project, which will have a permanent effect on the scenic resources of the valley."

When Orange & Rockland petitioned for a rehearing, conservationists and citizens' groups intensified their protest against the transmission line. Many wanted no power line, period. The conservationists also opposed underground power lines on the proposed mountain route.

Rockland County officials broke the impasse by asking the commission to help find a new route for the power line altogether. Mr. Carl J. Mays, executive director of the commission, said he was deeply concerned with the power problem and, "we intend to study existing lines and all proposals for new generating facilities and possible future lines to determine what impact such projects will have on the region."

Then began an extraordinary two months of meetings of county, town, and village officials, representatives of power companies and state experts in electrical power and conservation. The commission, meanwhile, deployed its own staff of experts and it began to map an alternative route well to the south of Buckberg Mountain. Members of citizens' groups were brought into these meetings in the new spirit of participatory democracy.

In September a Rockland County committee, aided at the working level by the Hudson River Valley Commission, found a compromise solution that was acceptable to the parties. The line was located around the base of Buckberg Mountain, although not as far away as the commission had

wanted. An existing power line across nearby mountains
would also be relocated on the new route. The commission summed up:

"This submission was approved by the HRVC and satis-
fied the demands of the citizens of the area. The line was
kept off the mountain, the valley was not marred by a new
slash across a prominent scenic resource, and the utility
company was able to thus avoid a long and costly legal battle with area citizens.

"The conservationists have saved the high route, and the
power line will take the low route," a local newspaper commented. The Federal Power Commission cited the Orange
& Rockland controversy as the best case history in the United
States of how the power-ecology dilemma can most sensibly
be resolved.

I sent the commission my own congratulations for a very
thorough job well done—an excellent example of how the
consultative process can still work in our country, even in
an age of polarization and confrontation.

We know we are going to need more electric power—
double the present capacity in New York State in twelve
years, eight times the 1970 capacity in the United States by
the year 2000. How far away from the critical public must
the new nuclear power plants be installed?

One possibility is the construction of nuclear power
plants on new man-made islands in offshore waters, founded
on the continental shelves. The sites would have to be en-
closed with larger cofferdams; then the islands would be
built, in part, out of solid wastes ferried out from coastal
cities. The nuclear power plants would be installed on the
new islands. Such sites are now being considered as part
of the work of the Atomic and Space Development Authority's Nuclear Power Siting Committee. Preliminary analysis
and discussions are already under way with utilities and
concerned agencies.

Mr. Charles F. Luce, chairman of the board of Con Edison, said he wanted to locate generating facilities on two islands off New York Harbor, each of them approximately eighty acres in area. There would be little thermal pollution of the ocean, and there would be relatively simple transmission to millions of people in coastal, urban regions. This new approach warrants careful evaluation. We must stimulate imaginative thinking about how the state's nuclear power siting program can best be carried out in the overall public interest. Mr. Luce's suggestion may well prove to be an important way to balance our need for electrical power and environmental protection in the rest of this century, but there can be no one solution. The quest for answers must be continuous, as we seek to improve power technology and make it more responsive to growing environmental awareness.

SIX

Open Spaces:
The Struggle for a More
Sensible Use of Land

When my brother Laurance and I were teenagers, we journeyed west one summer with our father and older brother, John, to spend a vacation on a tour of national parks.

For two days we stayed near Mesa Verde, a tableland some twenty miles long and two thousand feet high in the southwestern corner of Colorado. Its rimrocks command the sweep of the horizon, into the Rockies and down to the desert, and its south side is laced with steep canyons. Here are the fabulous cliff dwellings, hundreds of them, abandoned two hundred years or more before Columbus.

From the porch of a temporary log cabin museum on the mesa top, Mr. Jesse Nusbaum, the park superintendent, showed us a silent honeycomb of dwellings, and he explained how the early Indians had progressed over the centuries from pit houses to cliff palaces. My father asked questions about how they farmed, how they obtained their water, as we began to clamber about the crevices and toe-holds in the rock. In the evening, we gathered at the edge of a ravine to watch an Indian pageant on the opposite cliff, and the chants of the Navajos rang across the western air in the glow of the fires.

Then we went to Yellowstone National Park, the nation's largest, created by President Ulysses S. Grant in 1872 for "the benefit and enjoyment of the people." We drove through the forests, marveled at the geysers, the falls, and the cliffs of black glass. Mr. Horace Albright, the park superintendent, later to become director of the National Park Service, talked with my father about the problems of keeping the roadsides clean. He also discussed ways to make the park even more accessible for the millions who would come there as the national population expanded.

For John, Laurance, and me, however, the high point came when we took off for a two-week packtrain trip in Montana, riding at the rate of ten to sixteen miles a day. There we first came to know the refreshing, inspiring silence of the wilderness.

During the next two years, my father helped set up a museum at Mesa Verde with the understanding, as he wrote Mr. Nusbaum, "that it is properly a government responsibility, and that the government will carry the load after private means has established its merit." He also financed the clearing of roadsides in Yellowstone. This experiment was so successful that the United States Congress instituted and paid for the roadside clean-ups that are now public policy in all national and most state parks. But my father had a larger idea in his mind. "Magnificent view of the Tetons," he wrote about his principal impression of the West in that golden year.

In 1926, two years later, we all went back to Mesa Verde, stopping off in Santa Fe, New Mexico, to see the collection of pueblo pottery stored in the basement of the Museum of New Mexico. This visit led to our family's decision to help

establish a Laboratory of Anthropology in Santa Fe. Once
again, at Mesa Verde, we experienced the sense of a wise
urban culture that had sadly drifted away. But it was to the
Grand Tetons in Wyoming that my father wanted to go—
and his breathtaking proposal was to acquire the whole of
the northern Jackson Hole Country from which the tall
mountains could best be seen—so he could give this land
to the nation.

"It appeared to me to be an ideal project," he explained,
and not only for scenic, recreational, and spiritual considerations. "Only through the preservation as a sanctuary of
the Jackson Hole Country can the buffalo, elk, moose, and
other animals be permanently maintained and preserved
from extinction in the West."

My father's "ideal project" turned out to be a rough one,
however. It caused confusion and misunderstanding about
his land purchases, complaints from cattlemen who feared
loss of their grazing lands, and opposition from communities
which feared loss of tax revenue. There was also criticism
of the Rockefeller name *per se*—a problem we have learned
to live with over the years, but never to enjoy.

"The Tetons present a picture of ever-changing beauty,"
my father continued to insist, even as the problems mounted
and at times seemed insoluble.

In 1929 the Grand Teton National Park in Wyoming
was in fact created—but without Jackson Hole, the valley
to the east from where the splendid peaks of the Tetons
can best be viewed. In 1943 the Jackson Hole National
Monument was created, but it was not until 1950 that the
Grand Teton National Park was fully enlarged to include
the vital valley lands. It was my brother Laurance, a working conservationist, who brought Father's dreams for this
beautiful region to fruition. As president of the Jackson
Hole Preserve, Incorporated, a conservation foundation, he
presented 33,000 acres to the federal government—along

with some expert ideas on their use. Other gifts made possible the creation of a wildlife preserve and a wide range of facilities for visitors to the Grand Tetons.

Laurance went on to buy and give to the government the land for the Virgin Islands National Park, and he is a moving force in the Palisades Interstate Park Commission in New York and New Jersey. He has helped in the establishment of several important private conservation agencies, such as the Conservation Foundation, an organization of brilliant professionals who specialize in research and public education in the best uses of land.

In 1958 Laurance's life as a businessman and conservationist reached a new level of influence when President Dwight D. Eisenhower appointed him chairman of the Outdoor Recreation Resources Review Commission. His assignment was nothing less than to draw up a resources plan for the whole country.

Thus, in 1959, when I was inaugurated as Governor of New York, I had the strongest possible family example and inspiration to achieve on the state level a measure of what my father and brother were accomplishing in conservation everywhere in the United States.

The challenge was clear. William H. Whyte, Jr., the author of *The Organization Man*, defined it, in an article he wrote for *Fortune* magazine, in these words:

"With characteristic optimism, most Americans still assume that there will be plenty of green space on the other side of the fence. But this time, there won't be.

"Already, huge patches of once-green countryside have been turned into vast, smog-filled deserts that are neither city, suburb nor country and each day, at a rate of some 3000 acres a day, more countryside is being bulldozed under.

"You can't stop progress, they say, yet much more of this kind of progress, and we shall have the paradox of prosperity lowering our real standard of living."

And so in one of my first major actions as governor, I set in motion the "Open Spaces" program through which, in the next ten years, the people of New York State would acquire more than 375,000 acres of park and recreation lands. This area would be equivalent to more than twenty Manhattan Islands or one Grand Teton National Park. Then I initiated the "Next Step" program, to develop a very broad range of recreational facilities everywhere in the state.

The cost of the two programs was projected at $500 million—making them the largest such activities ever undertaken at the state level in the history of the United States.

The Open Spaces program began with a survey by the State Conservation Department of New York's present and future recreational needs. Our field men reported on specific locations and potential uses of tracts of land for recreational development. We compiled volumes of data in Albany, and we drafted briefings and brochures for members of the legislature, the press, and the public.

One of our most effective messages was a letter-size folder sent to every municipal official in New York State. It explained a plan by which municipalities might receive $3 of state funds for every $1 of their own for land acquisition in the event the legislation was approved by the people. This idea was so popular that Open Spaces was approved overwhelmingly by the voters of the State in 1960, with a bond issue of $75 million. This was later supplemented by an additional $25 million—making a total of $100 million for land acquisition alone.

The Park and Recreation Land Acquisition Bond Act in fact set up a new principle in the role of the state. It authorized grants-in-aid to municipalities of all kinds to assist them in the purchase of land for outdoor recreation. This was an example of the federal system of government at work on a joint enterprise, and it differed from the more familiar pattern of financing in which the state or a locality simply acquired things on its own.

Open Spaces moved off to a fast start in January 1961. The State Council of Parks rapidly committed the first $20 million. Out of eighteen new state parks, fifteen were located on waterfronts on Long Island Sound, the Great Lakes, the Niagara and St. Lawrence rivers, the Finger Lakes, and along interior streams. More than half of thirty-six additions to existing state parks also involved acquisition of waterfront property. In all, more than twenty-five miles of valuable salt and fresh water frontage were acquired during this period for the people of the state.

For state land other than parks, we signed more than 550 agreements for the purchase of some 100,000 acres, forty-two miles of fishing rights, and seventeen boat launching sites, at a cost of $5,200,000. With camping the fastest-growing outdoor recreation activity, we expanded and improved thirty-eight public campsites in the northern and central forests. The State Conservation Department also drafted plans for the construction of at least 250 boat launching sites.

We moved under Open Spaces to acquire more state lands in the historic, 9000-square-mile Forest Preserve area of the Adirondack and Catskill mountains, the state's priceless heritage, designated by Constitutional Amendment in 1895 to remain "forever wild." We quickly acquired approximately 40,000 acres, and set an early goal of 200,000 acres. The enthusiasm was spreading throughout our administration. Mr. C. W. Mattison, the land acquisition consultant for the Conservation Department, enthused in a speech at Higgins Lake, Michigan:

"The multiple use principle of land management grows in importance as the population expands. Land acquisition in New York is in high gear. The Conservation Department will keep it going. New York is serious about land for a bright future for its people."

Under the multiple-use concept, we encouraged a major expansion of forest products industries which might bring more jobs. The Conservation and Commerce departments surveyed public and private lands, and started a fruitful campaign to bring in forest industries to suitable sites. We encouraged research in new uses of wood. We offered technical assistance, Point Four style, to owners of woodlots with emphasis on product development and more sophisticated marketing. We even kept the industry informed on new developments and processes in forest product industries elsewhere in the United States and in the world.

The Division of Fish and Game, crippled for lack of funds when I took office, was granted a $600,000 cash advance for its Conservation Fund, and vital programs were quickly restored. Under the Wildlife Management Act, which had opened up almost a quarter of a million acres of private land to hunters, we increased the salaries of game protectors and entitled them Conservation Officers. We installed a statewide system of radio communication between these men. We appointed an advisory committee to aid in a parallel development of fisheries. We also began a ten-year campaign to remove billboards and other eyesores.

In recreational terms, we increased the capacity of our state parks by more than 14 per cent in my first term as governor, to 800,000 people admissible at any one time. We increased our $2.6 billion tourist industry by a very sturdy 30 per cent. We increased the number of campers by more than 50 per cent, with 134,000 people served every year in Conservation Department campsites from Long Island Sound to the Niagara Frontier.

But visits to state parks would increase from 30 million in 1960 to 47.5 million in 1970 to an estimated 56 million by 1980. Visits to forest recreation lands would increase from

4 million in 1960 to 6 million in 1970 to a projected 9 million in 1980.

So I went to the state legislature with the "Next Step" program for recreational development and won the endorsement, cooperation, and warm understanding of the legislators. The people of the state voted their endorsement of a $200 million bond issue to finance the program. This alone was double the size of the original Open Spaces investment. But the objective of the Next Step program was nothing less than to improve the quality of life in the state and to set an example to the nation. Specifically, I asked for:

35 beaches,
25 pools,
100 picnic areas,
20 golf courses,
40 harbors of refuge,
150 boat launching sites,
250 marine facilities,
600 waterway improvement projects,
40 nature centers,
10,000 campsites,
500 miles of hiking trails,
400 miles of riding trails,
400 miles of stream improvement,
400 miles of hunter access,
10,000 acres of wetlands development,
600 acres of city parks and playgrounds, and
Restoration of historic sites and other necessary constructions and acquisitions.

The legislature approved this ten-year program and it is now being implemented.

In April 1970 we designated a four and one half mile stretch of beach, drifting sand dunes, and valuable wetlands at the eastern end of Lake Ontario as a "natural beach." This meant that the beach, known as the Lakeview Game Management Area, would be preserved "forever wild." But the adjacent Southwick Beach State Park provides excellent facilities for swimming, camping, and picnicking, and access to the wild natural beach. Visitors may stroll anywhere among the dunes of the natural beach, enjoy the scenery, photograph the wild life. But they may not remove or destroy plants, dispose of refuse, make any unnecessary noise, use any form of motorized equipment, build fires, hunt or trap.

INDUSTRY VS. RECREATION—ONE SOLUTION

The struggle to save the environment demands much more than the development of massive government programs and the "selling" of those programs to the public. Frequently, we must fight sharp skirmishes with industrial and local community interests in the larger interest of the people of the state as a whole.

A prime example of how various and sometimes conflicting interests can be happily resolved is what happened on the east side of the Hudson Highlands, across the river from that embattled hydroelectric plant project on Storm King Mountain. Late in 1964 the State Council of Parks (now the State Council of Parks and Outdoor Recreation) began an investigation on the lower Hudson Valley looking toward the safeguarding of potential parklands on the one hand and balanced development on the other hand. A special Hudson Highlands Committee of the council, which did the work, rated the scenic highlands opposite Storm King as parkland. Their findings were backed up by the Hudson River Valley Commission, which gave the area a high priority for preservation as a park.

Suddenly, however, our long-range planning blew up in our faces—or so it seemed at the time. The Georgia-Pacific Corporation of Portland, Oregon, a timber company, made "firm plans" to build a wallboard factory at the foot of Mount Taurus, the key section of the Hudson lands we were earmarking for posterity. Georgia-Pacific had in fact secured the approval of the local governments, which wanted the tax revenues, and most of the residents, who wanted the jobs.

I got the president of Georgia-Pacific on the phone, and I said to him, "Look, we'd love to have you in New York State, but not *there*." I explained to him our intention to set aside this beautiful part of the valley as a scenic and recreational area. I made it quite plain that we wanted the new plant, we wanted the tax revenues, we wanted the jobs, but not in that particular spot. And I offered to help his company find a site for the wallboard plant somewhere else in our great state.

Whether he was surprised to get the phone call from me, whether he was hurt he could not build at the foot of Mount Taurus, or whether he was delighted at my offer to help out somewhere else, I do not know. But his attitude was entirely reasonable. He said, "O.K."

We moved fast to acquire that section of the Hudson Highlands before anybody else could get there. We had to, because the towns in the area were furious at us for detouring Georgia-Pacific—and they wanted to know what else we had in mind.

Late in 1967 we announced the creation of the new Hudson Highlands State Park, 2500 acres in size, embracing Mount Taurus, Little Stony Point, Breakneck Ridge, Sugar Loaf Mountain, and Bannerman's Island in the Hudson River. The island was named for a dealer in military equipment who bought it for storage of Spanish-American War surplus and later built a Scottish Castle on it.

But this is not all there is to the story of the new Hudson Highlands State Park, which I was to dedicate in the spring of 1970 as the 127th unit in the state park system. The 670 acres of Breakneck Ridge, the centerpiece of the three mountains forming the eastern side of the Hudson Gorge, were owned by the Central Hudson Gas & Electric Corporation, and the company's purpose in buying the land was to hold it for possible construction of a pumped-storage generating plant at some future time. But Mr. Lelan F. Sillin, Jr., then president of Central Hudson, agreed to turn over Breakneck Ridge to us at cost—if it could be preserved as part of a major park complex. This was a splendid gesture, wise and professional, but also warm and personal.

Then my brother Laurance, who had been the moving force in the surveys and activities to preserve these parklands, was heard from once again in a decisive capacity. It will be recalled that he was president of Jackson Hole Preserve and as such had been instrumental in pushing through my father's dream for the Grand Tetons and in creating the Virgin Islands National Park, which was Laurance's own magnificent contribution to our country. Laurance had also devised the matching funds idea for our Open Spaces program in New York State. Now Laurance told me that Jackson Hole Preserve would match dollar for dollar whatever New York State would put up to acquire land for the new Hudson Highlands State Park. This was a marvelous offer. The total cost was in the region of $3 million. Jackson Hole did contribute its half, including special grants to the nearby towns of Philipstown and Fishkill to compensate them for loss of tax revenue. These in-lieu-of-tax payments were slated to continue for five years, and they are in effect at time of writing.

This was an amazingly flexible—and constitutional—use of public and private money jointly to solve a community problem.

Meanwhile, we did not neglect Georgia-Pacific. We helped them locate peaceably and happily farther downstream at Indian Point, where a modern, industrial complex is growing in the vicinity of Consolidated Edison's nuclear power plant. This was one of the very rare instances of land use planning in which everybody came out smiling.

Laurance also played a key role, as chairman of the

State Council of Parks and Outdoor Recreation, in the state's acquisition in 1970 of 6725 acres of mountain wilderness in Ulster County, two hours from Manhattan, to be developed as the Minnewaska State Park. Many public and private groups, including the Nature Conservancy, joined hands in a dramatic rescue mission which saved these beautiful lands from a mortgage foreclosure and sale for commercial development.

SAVING AGRICULTURAL LAND

In the spring of 1966 I established a New York State Commission on the Preservation of Agricultural Land. In 1968 I also established an Agricultural Resources Commission. My objective is to make sure that our own and our coming generations will be able to maintain an adequate reserve of productive agricultural land in the midst of urbanization and rapid population growth.

Agriculture in New York State has immense vitality. But farming is keenly competitive, especially in periods of rapid technological change, when large funds must be invested in new equipment. Since farm incomes are not high, relatively speaking, and ready cash is short and costly, farm lands are peculiarly vulnerable to urban penetration. Land sold near cities by retiring farmers often goes for prices far in excess of what beginning farmers are able to afford. Thus the land tends to pass to real estate developers, to non-farm industries, or simply to individual investors who acquire the land only to hold it until the tide of urbanization reaches their property—and they can cash in.

Fortunately, New York and most other states still have room for agricultural and urban growth, though we need to choose much more wisely the direction of each. Farmers are producing more than ever before on half the land they once farmed. But their need for *good* land is urgent. Modern farming requires sizable fields suitable for the deployment of machines, and soils that will respond well to fertilization, hybrids, and other new elements of agricultural technology. Urban expansion, if wisely directed, may be channeled around such farm land.

In its first report to me, New York State's pioneering Agricultural Resources Commission recommended the immediate identification of all "valuable and productive" agricultural land in New York State. These will fall into three categories: muckland; tree fruit, vineyard, and similarly irreplaceable resources; and high-producing farm land of all types. Within these "Prime Agricultural Districts," it is proposed that the right of eminent domain be drastically modified—that it no longer be possible to restrict farm activities except by ordinances essential to public health and safety. The extension of "service districts" would be channeled by zoning and other means away from the prime agricultural districts.

Similarly, development of new homes in clusters rather than by random siting would save the prime agricultural districts from the scattering of residential neighborhoods and the gradual encroachment upon good farm lands.

The commission also recommended tax incentives for farmers who choose to stay on the farm—a plan to discourage land speculation in the prime agricultural districts. If the owners of prime lands do not use them for agricultural purposes for a specified period, the land would be taxed more heavily on its value for potential development. The commission recommended a survey to be made of the impact of existing tax laws which defer for five years real estate taxes on farm capital improvements and additions.

SOLID WASTES—10 POUNDS PER AMERICAN

In recounting these environmental issues, it is well to remind ourselves that the ultimate survival of human life on this planet will depend on man's ability to consult and to cooperate with his fellow man in preserving a livable environment. It is well to remember that we are truly our own worst enemies—all of us—and nowhere is this more evident than in the rubbish heaps we have created—all of us. In fact, no problem of land pollution is more critical to the cities, suburbs, and rural communities of America than the disposal of this rubbish—the so-called solid wastes.

Public and private sanitation agencies employ more than 337,000 men as collectors or drivers—one for every 590 people in the United States. They collect an average of 5.3 pounds of solid waste per day for each man, woman, and child in the country. But the actual amount of solid waste generated per capita is approximately 10 pounds per day, for 12 per cent of the population lives in communities that have no waste collection service at all.

There are about ten thousand authorized land disposal sites in the nation. Of these, only 6 per cent qualify as sanitary landfills. The other 94 per cent are potential sources of disease and pollution.

The present inadequate land disposal areas occupy nearly 600 square miles, most of it in or near populated areas where land is scarce and costly. To upgrade even the existing dumps to sanitary landfills, which consume land at a 71 per cent faster rate than open dumping, would require the immediate acquisition of more than 400 square miles of additional land. In addition, the per capita generation of solid waste is increasing rapidly while our population continues to expand. If projections for the New York region can be applied to other large urbanized areas, the amount of solid waste in the nation's metropolitan regions can be expected to more than triple by the year 2000. A projection for the Washington, D.C., metropolitan region indicates that solid waste generation there will nearly quadruple by the end of this century.

While most communities in the United States provide some form of public waste collection, only a tiny fraction make any attempt to reduce the volume of solid waste prior to disposal, other than by open burning, which in turn pollutes the air. In the entire country, the number of incinerators operated by public or private waste disposal agencies is estimated at three hundred—and many of these are so inefficient that they may not be worth the manpower required to run them. Composting plants and other systematic waste reclamation facilities are even rarer.

This reflects the reluctance of municipalities to invest in those aspects of sanitation that are rarely seen by the average citizen. Local expenditures for solid waste sanitation run about 80 per cent for collection as against 20 per cent for disposal.

If we are to make headway in solving the nation's waste disposal problems, we must approach them simultaneously from several angles. First, we must develop and build the equipment needed to reduce all solid waste to minimum volume before its ultimate disposal. Second, we must find ways to cut back or eliminate the production of materials that present severe disposal problems—those that do not rot, do not rust, or cannot be incinerated without releasing air pollution.

Specifically, we must obtain maximum compliance by industry and by the general public in the proper disposal of solid waste. We must provide incentives to industry to develop economically feasible techniques for salvaging metals and other potentially reusable materials from solid waste. We must obtain maximum thoroughness and speed at the local level in the collection of solid waste and its movement to proper disposal facilities.

A bill now before the United States Congress under the sponsorship of New York Congressman Hamilton Fish proposes the creation of a Solid Waste Management Trust Fund. The fund would derive its revenues entirely from disposal charges placed on products at the point of manufacture or importation. Up to two thirds of the income from the trust fund would be made available to the Secretary of Health, Education and Welfare, who would make grants from such funds to state, interstate, regional, and municipal government bodies for the more efficient disposal of solid waste. At least one third of the income from the trust fund, for an initial period of five years, would be made available to a new Federal Solid Waste Management Corporation for research and development of improved waste disposal techniques, equipment, and construction and operation.

Our ultimate objective ought to be the development, through federal-state-local cooperation, of a coordinated, nationwide system of solid waste processing centers. But we have a long way to go. Senator Charles E. Goodell of New York recently called for establishment of mandatory federal standards and enforcement for the disposal of solid waste because "there simply are no federal standards or enforcement procedures." Mr. Carl L. Klein, Assistant Secretary of the Interior for Water Quality and Research, said current laws were as useful as a "wet noodle."

But there are many great new ideas about how to handle solid waste, and some of them might well be useful. One is a proposal for an incinerator ship, which will load up garbage like cargo at ports, sail away, grind it all up, and dump it, far, far out at sea.

"Mount Trashmore" is a working reality in Illinois. This is a honeycomb of cells of garbage, covered by earth, rising to a planned height of 125 feet. When it is complete, toboggan runs and ski slopes will be built down its sides.

Already, all kinds of compactors are in use. These can exert pressures which can tear a telephone book, fold cans into tin leaves, or smash automobiles to relatively small squares of scrap. "Biodegradable" products are coming on the market. These break down or disintegrate after use, like the recording tapes on which instructions are delivered to the secret agents of *Mission Impossible.*

There are spectacular ideas. One is to unleash the power of the hydrogen bomb against solid waste at regional salvage dumps. A fusion torch, directed at an automobile, will make it disappear. Superfreezing with so called cryogenic agents can also reduce solid waste to powder.

A CITIZENS' "CLEAN-IN"

But the simplest and one of the very best ideas is a citizen drive, everywhere in the United States, against litter pollution. One of my young volunteer workers in New York City recently recommended to me:

"One Saturday afternoon, beginning at twelve o'clock, the people should turn out to clean up their respective neighborhoods. For once, on a weekend, we could see New York a sparkling and beautiful city and enjoy walking through our parks and streets, without litter and filth.

"If our air and water pollution cannot be cleaned up immediately, then at least we can live and walk in a decent city. We can be proud we've shown we care. Who knows, we might even meet our neighbors.

"Very simply, this would be New York's Clean-In. It would be like Earth Day. If it works, we could repeat it once a year. Once a month. Once a week. I hope this idea can be passed along, and maybe we can get going on it."

I am pleased to say that more than 3700 young people took part in a seven-week Hometown Beautification Program in New York State during the summer of 1970. A total of 204 communities, more than three times the number which participated in the first year of the Hometown Beautification Program in 1965, cooperated with our Division for Youth to provide a summer work experience between July 1 and Labor Day. Since the program was launched, some 15,000 young people have worked at a wide range of projects. They are transforming delinquent tax properties into "vest pocket parks," developing picnicking and swimming areas, conservation study trails and fishing and boating facilities. They are planting flowers in parks and restoring local sites of historic interest.

We allocated a total of $1,146,000 to the Division for Youth in 1970–71 for the Hometown Beautification Program.

A recent editorial in *The New York Times* approached the same problem from a different point of view:

"Granted the staggering problems of a great city, from paralyzed traffic to narcotics in the schools, and the time required to ease them, New York could still be made a more livable community than it is," said the *Times.* "It is not true that the gutters of a city must be inches thick with trash because illegally parked cars prevent street sweepers from flushing it out. Nor is it an immutable law that slum alleyways and air shafts must be fetid with garbage because derelict landlords provide no receptacles.

"Neither is it true that nothing can be done to keep streets and parks alike from serving as dumping grounds for discarded newspapers, candy wrappers, beer cans and plastic bags.

"These depressing manifestations—as well as vacant lots piled high with illegally dumped rubbish, hulks of abandoned cars left for weeks to rust in the streets of Brooklyn and the Bronx, and soot from oilburners and faulty incinerators—are not inevitable attributes of city life.

"They are the consequences of failure to enforce the law, failure to use imaginatively the manpower and resources available, failure to make it plain that the City of New York will not tolerate the willful despoiling of the community, whether it is done systematically by a landlord or casually by a lout."

In truth, we need the idealism and faith of the young man proposing a citizen Clean-In as well as the indignation of the editorial writer. And, as a state, we are making progress against the solid waste problem.

Effective in January of 1963, we outlawed the open dump. We required that refuse sites be operated as true sanitary landfills, and that municipal incinerators be operated so as not to create a nuisance or a hazard to public health. In 1962 there were more than 1600 open dumps in the state. In 1970 we now have 921 land disposal sites, of which more than 50 may be classified as sanitary landfills. The elimination of almost 700 open dumps has been due to Health Department pressure, but often the managers of the dumps proved able to delay proceedings for months, even years. When the question of new sites came up, invariably the answer of residents was, "Who wants garbage in their backyard?"

In 1966 I proposed that the state take a larger look at the whole problem and prepare a statewide plan for the disposal of solid wastes. The Health Department launched comprehensive surveys on amounts, methods, and locations of waste disposal in nine counties and in New York City. This cost the state $750,000, and we also obtained $230,000 of federal money for this project. We have since appropriated an additional $883,000 for studies of twelve more counties. Our objective is to complete our statewide plan by 1972. The State Pure Waters Authority, incidentally, has also been engaged to run municipal solid waste disposal systems, and to arrange financing.

Our experience to date shows that large sites will have to be acquired for sanitary landfills five years in advance of the need. These should be fitted into ultimate land-use plans and Open Spaces programs of the future. Landfill sites ought also to be useful for construction sites, for recreational grounds and, at the very least, as open space buffer zones between industrial districts.

The state budget for 1970–71 provides $200,000 to help municipalities plan for the construction of waste disposal facilities, $50,000 to train operators in modern techniques of sanitary landfill and incineration, and $100,000 to provide for testing and research in experimental new waste treatment methods.

How, then, to bring Open Spaces right into the cities and how to bring city dwellers out to the Open Spaces in greater numbers?

In the core of the cities, recreational opportunities are limited. The relative absence of recreational facilities in the slums is a very real grievance of the poor. States and localities, in my judgment, must give major consideration to recreation needs in their programs for development in urban areas. In New York City, for example, we are developing a full-scale cultural complex along with a new state office building in Harlem. This will include an auditorium for meetings and dances, a theater to be used by community groups and traveling companies, and space for museum and exhibition activities.

The federal urban renewal program needs revision to give more emphasis to recreational needs. Parks, sports grounds, and community centers must rank in importance with housing—vital as it is to start making headway against the critical shortage of housing. The creative use of waterfront fill-in areas, of air rights, and of obsolete rights of way, for example, will provide room for fun without taking away land needed for housing and commercial growth.

Federal surplus land in urban areas, where practical, should be made available to public agencies without charge for recreational and other appropriate purposes—and this should be done now. Unneeded defense installations in and around cities will be particularly suitable for recreational purposes. Old airfields can be turned into playgrounds and parks, and developed for multiple use.

The need to transform our urban core areas into decent

places to live in and work in is a priority domestic challenge confronting this nation. No longer can we tolerate the decay, degradation, and despair that exist there; no longer can we ignore the discontent that breeds there.

THE URBAN DEVELOPMENT CORPORATION—A NEW APPROACH

Since its creation in the spring of 1968, New York State's Urban Development Corporation has taken a total approach in generating dynamic community development, tying in housing, transportation, jobs, education, and the other factors which create a balanced, vital environment.

In 1970 we are aiming at construction starts on approximately ten thousand housing units, at an estimated total cost in excess of $300 million, in communities from one end of the state to the other. We are also undertaking a variety of nonresidential projects. The complete development of current projects will fully commit UDC's entire initial $1 billion bond authorization.

The UDC legislation highlights the particular importance of the private sector by calling for the sale or lease of UDC's interest in projects to private enterprise at the earliest feasible time. Clearly, private capital, private entrepreneurs, and private experience are crucial if the people are to receive optimum benefits from our new initiative.

UDC has the power to condemn real property and the power to override local ordinances. It has a full range of development powers from planning to construction to management, exercised in partnership with private enterprise. Funds from the State of New York to initiate and carry out projects are directly available to UDC through repayable first-instance appropriations and through revenue bonds authorized by the UDC Act.

In all communities in which we are active, we have sought to establish a working partnership with local civic leaders, local public officials, local community residents, and local developers. We have viewed our role as a catalytic one, doing things which are not easily done by established public or private enterprises.

While low-income families have the greatest need for housing, an acute need also exists for families with moderate and middle incomes. It is our view that developments which cater *exclusively* to low-income families are undesirable. They tend to produce large-scale, institutionalized, *apartheid* projects of questionable value either to society as a whole or to the low-income families so housed.

UDC housing, therefore, seeks to provide for a cross section of age groups and income levels in a diversified community, where the elderly are not isolated from the young. This leads to a 70-20-10 formula—70 per cent of all housing units on a particular site for middle- and moderate-income families, 20 per cent for low-income families and 10 per cent for the elderly. This housing mix may vary, depending on the project and local needs.

On May 21, 1969, Mayor Lindsay and I announced details of a new UDC/New York City partnership. The new program will result in the construction of at least twelve thousand new units of housing for all income ranges. Development cost will be more than $350 million. The city is subsidizing the projects mainly through land write-down, relocation of site occupants, and necessary demolition. Design and development will be sponsored by UDC.

In my opinion, this agreement between the city and the state represents the kind of cooperative action we must take to solve the urban crisis in the United States. It is also critical to the improvement of our environment and the quality of life.

The development of Welfare Island is the largest and most exciting of UDC's New York City projects. The plan calls for the creation of a new Island Town on this sliver of land in the East River. Twenty thousand people from all income groups will live there, overlooking the East River, Queens, and Manhattan, shopping in a unique Town Center arcade and enjoying parks provided for all citizens of New York.

The plan calls for the retention of the existing hospitals and important architectural landmarks, for the exclusion of cars—restricting traffic to service and emergency vehicles—and for a mini-transit system. All public facilities will be provided along with the housing.

The project, to be supervised by a Welfare Island Development Corporation, will be financed by UDC and by other public and private sources, outside the city's debt limit. Construction is to begin no later than June 23, 1971.

The result will be a completely new community, a new neighborhood, a new asset for New York City—and a hopeful new example in environmental planning that may be followed everywhere in the United States.

The Syracuse Central Business District has had a recent building boom, but Syracuse, like all American cities, is facing severe urban problems. So UDC, at the request of former Mayor William Walsh, agreed to undertake one commercial and two residential development projects.

The $25 million Clinton Square Plaza urban renewal project is adjacent to Clinton Square, through which the Erie Canal once ran. UDC was asked to assist the project after private attempts to develop it proved fruitless. Two and one half blocks of deteriorated commercial structures will be removed and replaced with a twenty-story office building, a four-story department store, 100,000 square feet of specialty shops, an enclosed mall, a hotel, and a 1200-car municipal garage. Construction was to begin in 1970.

A 200-unit high-rise apartment building is also to be built in the Near East Side Urban Renewal Project area near downtown Syracuse. The $5 million project is being undertaken in cooperation with the Syracuse Community Housing Development Corporation, a group of business and civic leaders. A construction start was expected in the fall of 1970.

Up to a thousand units of housing will be built in the Syracuse Hill Neighborhood Development Program area. This construction will be carried out in cooperation with the University Hill Corporation and the Syracuse Community Housing Development Corporation. Ground will be broken in 1971.

In both of these residential projects, the Syracuse Housing Authority has agreed to lease 30 per cent of the units, 20 per cent for low-income families, and 10 per cent for the elderly.

In New York State, completely new communities are receiving increasing attention in our struggle to improve the environment. UDC has two new town projects, one in Amherst, near Buffalo, and another in Lysander, near Syracuse.

Amherst is the site of a new campus for the State University of New York. The new campus will result in a projected increase of Amherst's population from 90,000 to 240,000 by the year 1985. To ensure that development in and around Amherst proceeds in a reasonably ordered manner, and to help the town meet the problems of rapid growth, I asked the UDC to serve as the vehicle for state cooperation in the development of the area immediately surrounding the new campus.

FOCUS ON THE CITIES

We are concentrating our Open Spaces program increasingly in the cities of New York State. And in doing this, we are not simply expressing goodwill or warm intent; we are investing large sums of money to improve the quality of urban life. We are also obtaining matching participation by the municipalities for our grants-in-aid.

In 1968, for example, the state authorized $830,250 for

the improvement of Baisley Pond Park, in the borough of
Queens in New York City. This involved the construction
of an outdoor swimming pool, bathhouse, diving pool, wad-
ing pool, sun decks, and terraces. Baisley Pond Park is located in a congested area otherwise lacking in recreational
facilities. We also allocated $439,000 for the development
of Cook Field in the city of Yonkers, comprising 35 acres
for ballfields, picnic areas, and shelters.

During 1968 and 1969 we invested $287,500 in the con-
struction of an educational center, nature trails, a wildlife
identification system, and landscaping in the Bronx, in New
York City. An amount of $74,436 was authorized for the
expansion of the Kingsley Street playground in the city of
Buffalo, and similar sums for downtown development in
smaller cities. In Syracuse we first spent $54,000 on the de-
velopment of court games, recreation areas, and playgrounds
in the heavily populated northern region. Then we added
$39,750 for the purchase and installation of three prefab-
ricated aluminum swimming pools with decks, fencing, and
self-contained purification equipment and showers. Later,
we provided $207,500 for the rehabilitation of bathhouses
and swimming pools at Thornden and McKinley parks in
Syracuse.

In Broome County, a state grant-in-aid of $210,675 was
made for the design and construction of an artificial skating
rink in Endicott. It will be available to more than 200,000
residents of the community. During the summer the new
rink will be converted for use for band concerts, picnics,
tennis, and street dancing.

In April of 1970 we approved nearly $1.8 million in
grants-in-aid to eighteen cities, suburbs, and small towns
for park construction, and also applied for an additional
$800,000 in federal aid for parks.

I would not want to leave any impression, however, that
the state accomplishes everything, and the localities nothing.
On the contrary, the level of municipal leadership in New

York State is very high. Westchester County, for one example, first established sewage systems for residential areas, Hudson River pollution abatement, Long Island Sound pollution abatement, open space park acquisition, and noise abatement programs. Westchester County built the first county sewer system, and was the first to set up a county sewer commission to coordinate plans. "Can you imagine the condition of Long Island Sound today if Westchester County had been asleep all these years?" asks County Executive Edwin G. Michaelian—and he is so right.

Westchester pioneered at county level the acquisition and maintenance of park and recreation areas. Westchester now owns almost 11,000 acres of prime park land, which it began to obtain in the 1920s. Recently, it has acquired 3500 more acres for its people.

While bringing parks to the cities, we must also do more to bring city people to the parks. New York State, for example, provides transportation annually for some 190,000 inner city residents to visit state parks. Approximately one third of these people are adults, mostly senior citizens. We offer all types of games and sports in the parks, story hours for young children, square dancing, social dancing, performing arts, and environmental education. The lure of the beaches is strong on Long Island, and the animal sanctuaries on Bear Mountain are popular. One of our counselors said, "Most of these youngsters never saw a crab or a live fish or even poison ivy. We want to give them a basic understanding of the living environment to take home."

But what they go home to is also the living environment, and this is what we must never lose sight of. To millions the city *is* the environment. It can be variety, opportunity, privacy, dynamism—and it can be rats biting children's fingers and toes. We need Open Spaces in the city more than anywhere else.

In December of 1969 I dedicated the first phase of the new Harlem River State Park in the Bronx, in New York

City. This park is particularly exciting and useful because it is located right in the middle of one of our most disadvantaged districts. I was delighted when the State Senate Minority Leader, Joseph Zaretzki, asked whether there might be a possibility for another state park on the opposite bank of the Harlem River.

This possibility—a real one—would create a splash of green, freedom to move, freedom to breathe, in the slums. This would change a river which, though less majestic than the Hudson, might well be the one along whose banks the real story of the next decade will be told.

SEVEN

The Arts and
the Quality of Life

The challenge today is not simply to alleviate the forces of crowding and noise, pollution and wastes. It is both larger and more subtle than that. The nature and quality of the lives all of us lead are shaped by the positive forces in our culture as well as the negative hazards of our environment. One of our concerns must therefore constantly be to lift the level of human awareness and perception, and to enhance the enjoyment of the world around us. For this, we look to the arts.

Now for some reason, politicians have a feeling that culture is a very dangerous subject and they should avoid it. But when I was fortunate enough to be elected Governor of New York, I decided I would share my enjoyment of some of the modern art objects I had collected with my fellow politicians in Albany.

Well, it was a new experience for Albany and for the legislators. They had never seen anything like it. I got the standard reaction: "My son, who is three years old, could have done better." It was delightful.

But the exciting and the interesting development was to

come. The legislators came to the Executive Mansion, with their wives, and little by little, they got used to the art. Soon they would come to see if there was anything new in the house. We had a list printed, which they could take home, containing the names of the artists and pertinent data.

A sculpture by Ibram Lassaw, the "Galaxy of Andromeda," created a tremendous stir in Albany when it arrived. Legislators thought it looked like a building after a fire!

Of course, no collection would be complete without a Sandy Calder mobile. Ours was called "Flying Boomerangs," on the ceiling of the gallery upstairs. All ages enjoyed this, believe me. Calder is easily understood.

A Lee Bontecou, untitled, one of the early ones, created quite a degree of excitement because it is three-dimensional, and people all want to know what the hole is for. The only thing I tell them is, "If you try to understand, you are lost. Just don't think. Just look and feel and register, and then go away and come back. That's the best way."

A Barbara Hepworth—"Green Globe"—is small but lovely if you get completely away from any link to reality. Legislators understand sculpture better than painting, I find.

In Albany, too, there is a delightful work, "Plumbob" by Yasuhide Kobashi. We can pull the bobs up and down, two of them on each string, so we make our own compositions. This is a great source of satisfaction, not only for the legislators but also for our children. It lets you participate, and participating is a very important part of life's enjoyment.

We also have some lithographs like "The Farm" by Emil Weiss after Van Gogh. Of course, the legislators felt very much at home with it. It is reassuring when they come across a picture of this kind. And Cézanne's "The Bathers" —they get concerned here with nudity, but it is something they have to get used to.

A Braque cubist "Composition" evokes the usual, "Well, my son did better in school."

A Miró is the painting the legislators really recognize. They think it is Fiorello La Guardia's hat. This is nostalgic for the New York City delegation, and stirs up a lot of enthusiasm.

IS MODERN ART A MENACE?

I will never forget the late Henry Luce, who was one of the great men of this country, one of the great patrons of the arts, and a trustee of the Museum of Modern Art. Just after World War II, he was very concerned about modern art. A new editor had just come from Yale to *Life* magazine, who made Mr. Luce feel that perhaps modern art was a dangerous factor threatening the strength of democracy. He said that he and his editors were considering whether they should expose and denounce it as a destructive force in America.

At the time, I was president of the Museum of Modern Art, and I said, "Harry, we all had better sit down and talk this over before you take a stand." William S. Paley, John Hay Whitney, Alfred Barr, and Rene d'Harnoncourt, who were also trustees of the museum, joined the discussion. First, we had dinner, and then we went on to the museum to talk some more—a sort of illustrated conversation. Alfred Barr was the principal philosopher of the evening. He said to Luce, "You're a missionary's son and I'm a missionary's son. I understand your concern and your point of view."

The fascinating thing about this experience is that we ended up the evening with Henry Luce being convinced that modern forms of artistic expression were the only area left in democracy where there was true freedom, where you had absolute freedom and there were "no holds barred." He changed from a deep concern that modern art was a destructive force to the conclusion that it was one of the great bastions of freedom and strength in our lives.

The arts are indeed a critical measure of "the quality

of life"—a fact that historians, if not always politicians, have recognized for centuries. We are constantly faced in government with combating the negative, inherited problems that have become too much for any other segment of society to handle—crime, poverty, drug addiction, to name a few. But the arts offer us the rare opportunity to further something that is positive—the expansion of human capacity and the pursuit of happiness—which is, after all, not only the central element of the arts, but of good government as well.

Twentieth-century man is so surrounded by mass production, by machines and anonymous consumer goods that his eye thirsts for individuality. He turns to art to enjoy individual expressiveness. Paintings and sculptures, artifacts created by individual hands and conceived by individual spirits, satisfy a craving for personality, for uniqueness.

My own love of the visual arts came from my mother, and it grew through my association of more than thirty years with the Museum of Modern Art. Mother, in turn, got this interest from her father, who was United States Senator Nelson Aldrich of Rhode Island, a collector of the art of Europe and of various early Mediterranean civilizations. Mother would have been classified as one of the avant-garde collectors in her day, and she was a founder of the Museum of Modern Art.

My interest in the performing arts grew with my friendship for Lincoln Kirstein and Eddie Warburg, fellow members of the Junior Advisory Committee of the Museum of Modern Art. Through them, I became interested in the founding of the School of American Ballet and the American Ballet under the leadership of George Balanchine, which has evolved into the superb New York City Ballet. Also through them, I became involved in the same period in the founding of the American Lyric Theatre, whose purpose was to encourage, support, and promote the musical, dramatic, and choreographic arts.

As Coordinator of Inter-American Affairs for President Franklin D. Roosevelt from 1940 to 1944, I arranged to send the American Ballet on a tour of Latin America. This was not only an exciting experience for the Latin Americans but also for Kirstein and Balanchine. They were truly pioneers in this first government-sponsored performing arts program abroad.

At the same time, I arranged through the Museum of Modern Art for the first government-sponsored traveling exhibitions of American art throughout the Western Hemisphere. This transition from private sponsorship of the arts to government sponsorship seemed like a natural and logical one at the time. However, it met with a great deal of reluctance on the part of the Congress.

When I was Undersecretary of Health, Education and Welfare during the early 1950s, Mrs. Oveta Culp Hobby, the Secretary of HEW, and I persuaded President Eisenhower to sponsor legislation to create a National Council on the Arts. Unfortunately, our senatorial sponsor could not resist an opportunity to be witty about the measure. He called it the "free piano-lesson bill"—and so our show closed out of town.

GOVERNMENT SUPPORT OF THE ARTS—BREAKTHROUGH IN NEW YORK STATE

As Governor of New York, I tried again to get legislative support of the arts. This time I was able to do better. I discovered that while I could not carry a tune, I could persuade a legislature. Thus in 1960, my second year as governor, a New York State Council on the Arts was enacted by the legislature at my request. This was the first organization of its kind to be created either at the state or the federal level—and all forty-nine other states and the federal government itself eventually followed our lead.

I believe the arts rank alongside international security,

foreign economic policy, and the pursuit of excellence in education as matters of central concern to our nation's welfare.

Many social and political forces have combined, at this moment in history, both to compel interest in the arts and to justify that interest in practical terms.

The intersection of these forces provides an unparalleled opportunity for the arts and the nation, particularly since it occurs at a moment when a surge of vitality in the arts themselves has brought their needs and their pleasures to the attention of the national consciousness as never before.

Wisely applied, all of these factors can lead to an environment more conducive to distinguished performance, to a larger and more appreciative audience, and to a higher level of artistic accomplishment.

I deeply believe that the ultimate test of democracy lies in the quality of the artistic and intellectual life it creates and supports. This is why, on the basis of our experience in New York, I can see a real validity to the concept that where eighteenth-century America was focused on achieving political democracy, and nineteenth-century America on economic democracy, this century may prove in the end to be the century of a new cultural democracy.

The arts are not for the privileged few—they are for the many, for the people as a whole. This is the central fact and the very essence of the strength of the arts in a democratic society. The values of the arts are universal: Everyone *can* feel the impact of cultural experiences, once his eyes and ears have been opened and his mind sensitized. There is no reason why anyone in our society should be denied the opportunity for these same experiences, the spiritual exhilaration that the arts offer.

To say that exposure to the arts can change the lives of the vast majority of our citizens would be an unnecessary overstatement. But the arts can add a new dimension: They can teach us to hear when we listen and see when we look. They can sensitize us, teach us to feel, and in the process, help to make us more complete human beings.

The impact of the arts goes far beyond the opera house, the concert hall, or the museum, needless to say. Our leading sociologists and educators insist that the arts are fundamental to the program for every student. The ability of the arts to reach out and create new enthusiasm for learning among children in slum areas is being proven day by day. Often, a child or adult may be better able to express himself or herself or to grasp a new concept when it is presented in terms of film, the dance, or theater.

The arts can also contribute to the quality of American life in everything from highway construction to graphic design, from urban planning to education, from communication media to environmental problems.

I would be the last person to maintain that governments should become the sole supporter or even the principal support of the arts in this country. The arts must continue to rely on individual effort, on individual benefactors, on private foundations, and on business. Those private sources, in fact, must be encouraged to increase their involvement with the arts if we are to be assured a stable cultural life. Nothing would be more deleterious than for those traditional sources to assume that increased governmental participation will relieve them of further responsibility.

But there is one aspect of the arts in which government is singularly able to make a significant contribution—making the arts as widely available to all the people as education or electricity.

In 1960 New York State developed a completely new concept for the support of the arts in the United States with the founding of the New York State Council on the Arts. We proved that government funds enhance artistic freedom, rather than restrict it. We proved that the arts can be good public policy, without becoming political. We proved that government funds can increase local and private support, rather than diminish it.

The bill to implement formation of the Council on the Arts was introduced early in the 1960 legislative session at my request. The only way I could get many of the legislators to take the bill seriously was to ask that it be tried as a temporary commission on a two-year basis—and, frankly, to ask some to vote for it as a personal favor.

As it turned out, this temporary basis gave us an unexpected plus. It permitted the council to conduct imaginative explorations without establishing irrevocable policies. The opportunity to gain practical experience through trial and error is essential to any undertaking to serve the public in the arts.

In any event, our legislation passed, and in January 1961 the council was formed, ably chaired by Seymour H. Knox and directed by Laurance Roberts, formerly director of the American Academy in Rome. Surveys were taken to list and evaluate the state's artistic resources. These ranged from specific performing facilities in fifty communities to what was generally available throughout the state.

We found that the arts tended to be concentrated in a few metropolitan areas. They were unavailable on a high level of quality to a broad geographic cross section of our population. Major professional organizations were not assuming their role as arts standard-bearers and arts standard-raisers. Artistic and managerial staffs were rarely compensated in any way equivalent to their efforts and talent. So we persuaded the legislature in 1961 to approve a $450,000 appropriation.

The question was raised whether the arts and the state's concern should not properly be the function of the educational system. I replied that support for the arts should be to promote the freedom which the creative nature of the artist demands—and to promote the availability of the arts to all the citizens of the state. The legislature's approval of this concept was the turning point.

In January 1961 Laurance Roberts went back to Italy and was succeeded by John MacFadyen as director. The council entered a period of experimental programing. Quality and individual creativity were established as the first criteria for state support of an artistic undertaking. The program evolved in three distinct areas—support for touring performances and exhibitions, technical assistance to the community, and special projects to "share the wealth" of talent throughout the state. Communities receiving help were required to develop private support as well for performances and presentations to specified limits.

In 1961 four professional companies gave 92 performances in 46 communities at a cost to the state council of $330,000. By the end of the 1964 season, 71 companies were giving 277 performances in 92 communities at a cost to the council of only $153,000—thanks to aroused community interest and support.

Meanwhile, the technical assistance program helped organizations at the community level, amateur and semiprofessional, to raise their standards. For example: coaching sessions for sections of community orchestras in the Adirondacks were conducted by sections of the Buffalo Philharmonic Orchestra. Seminars and workshops were held in set design, directing, and all aspects of community theater, led by what we might term the brightest lights of Broadway.

In 1964–69, the new executive director, John B. Hightower, a dynamic young leader, engaged in a variety of projects directed toward the education and growth of audiences. The council was graduated from the ranks of the temporary and became by law a permanent part of state government. The council brought the Metropolitan Opera Studio, contemporary and Shakespearean theater, philharmonic orchestras, and the New York City Ballet to many parts of our state where they had never been seen before. It also helped to organize local arts councils throughout the state. The Council on the Arts was instrumental in cataloguing and preventing destruction of beautiful and architecturally significant buildings. It assisted local art and historical museums, sponsored ten touring exhibitions of art, and arranged for self-contained touring exhibits in the decorative arts. It undertook a pilot project for extended loan exhibitions from the Metropolitan Museum of Art in New York City to upstate communities. It prepared a two-part art exhibit for the New York State Pavilion at the World's Fair.

In Buffalo in 1969 there was a standout success when the council and the Buffalo Philharmonic Orchestra introduced a house guest for a week. This was the entire New York City Ballet of George Balanchine. But this was far more than a concert appearance. The New York City Ballet acted for the week as a "company in residence." It held master classes, lecture demonstrations, and gave introductory performances in dance and interviews for students of dance no matter what their age.

The programs of the New York State Council on the Arts have reached 340 communities across the state. Community arts councils have grown to more than 450. The legislature has hailed the arts as "a vital aspect of our culture and heritage." Skeptics, they were no more.

In the mid-1960s, we completed the New York State Theater in Lincoln Center in New York City. The state investment was $15 million. We also participated in the construction of the $4 million Saratoga Performing Arts Center, opened in 1966. The center's theater, with its open sides, is among the world's largest. The center attracts an estimated 200,000 visitors to Saratoga Springs each year and brings cultural benefits to upstate New York of a quality that usually is available only in the large metropolitan centers.

The New York State Museum in Albany plans, designs, produces, and displays exhibits dealing with history and ecology. Its 300,000 visitors a year now constitute the largest single audience at a state-operated cultural institution.

The New York State Library makes its extensive collections available throughout the state. Its collections include approximately four million volumes. The state also provides general aid to the public libraries of New York, serving virtually all of the state's residents, with an annual appropriation on the scale of $15 million.

The New York State Council on Architecture, established in 1966, acts to encourage and stimulate interest in architectural excellence in construction. It assists municipalities in the restoration of buildings of historic interest which are intended for public use. Under the $1.4 billion State University Construction Fund, we are seeking architectural creativity—and we are translating it into brick, glass, stone, and steel. At each of the fifty-eight campuses of the university across the state, a supervising architect is given the responsibility not only for the expanding campus but also for relating that campus to the community as a whole.

In 1966 my associates and I proposed and the legislature approved the Natural Beauty Commission, empowered to develop programs for enhancement of natural resources and to promote aesthetic considerations in state construction. We also created a New York State Historic Trust, first in the nation, to identify, acquire, and operate historic sites.

THE ARTS EXPLOSION IN THE U.S.

It is not inappropriate at this point to remember that half the population of the United States is under twenty-eight years of age. The lives, the thoughts, the actions of the younger half are already beginning to affect the nation. Studies have indicated that the percentage of college graduates who want to pursue business careers, for instance, is decreasing. As an indication of where they are going, applications from Yale undergraduates to the graduate School of Art and Architecture are three times the number of applications that were made only four years ago. These men and women are fueling the demand for cultural facilities.

Everywhere in the United States, people are responding to the arts as never before. The reasons and the results are good for business and good for politics. Some three hundred new arts organizations throughout the country were given tax-exempt status in 1966 alone. Forty of these were formed in California.

The statistics of the arts explosion in the United States in the 1960s are almost unbelievable. In 1966 the new arts organizations included 43 arts councils, 35 theater groups, 12 opera groups, 12 museums, 55 historical societies, 14 art centers, 45 music organizations, 15 dance or ballet groups, 30 art groups, 16 education-in-the-arts groups, and 10 miscellaneous organizations active in photography and architecture, etc.

In New York the experience of one of our industrial cities, Syracuse, was wonderful and startling. During the 1966 season in Syracuse, population 212,000, the arts outdrew baseball five to one. The audience for arts events was nine times greater than the total attendance at all conventions, conferences, and trade shows; 583 individual arts programs were presented for 906 performances and approximately one twelfth of the population was engaged in producing the local arts events. The cash outlay by those who produced, taught, learned, or attended music, drama, or dance events amounted to more than $2,420,000.

Between 1960 and 1965 the number of arts organizations in Syracuse increased 82 per cent, the total number of arts programs increased 87 per cent, and the total number of artistic performances rose 43 per cent.

Everywhere in the United States, other cities had similar experiences. Huntsville, Alabama, found a painless way of supporting the arts—a 10 per cent tax on drinks at all clubs. The funds go toward a new arts center—and amount to

$250,000 a year. Seattle, Portland, Tulsa, San Diego, and Honolulu have raised funds for local arts organizations through annual auctions. In Seattle the results have yielded an average annual income of $125,000 to strengthen local groups. Winston-Salem, Fort Wayne, St. Paul, Quincy, and St. Louis are contributing well-directed and sizable annual funds to community arts projects and institutions.

The arts explosion in the United States also generates economic growth. The general economy of Saratoga during the months of July and August increased $2,000,000 over the year before the opening of the Saratoga Performing Arts Center. During the first season of the center, sales of a typical downtown retailer increased 21 per cent. Another merchant threatened by bankruptcy in 1965 survived financially despite the emergence of six new competing stores in the area.

But even while we were helping bring the arts to more people than ever before, our cultural heartland was undergoing serious erosion. Costs were increasing to the point that many of our largest and most renowned operas, concert orchestras, ballet companies, and theater aggregations were losing a fortune. Often, their deficits were accumulating to the point of bankruptcy. The New York City Center of Music and Drama was running an estimated deficit of $2,400,000 in the spring of 1970. The New York City Opera was $1,300,000 in the red. The estimated deficit of the Buffalo Philharmonic Orchestra was $634,500.

It seemed to me the state had a responsibility to act. So I asked the legislature to appropriate $18 million for a program of direct state aid to cultural organizations. This extended our previous financing of the State Council on the Arts ninefold. To their credit, in a time of intense competition for every tax dollar, the legislators recognized the priority. Our program was approved.

I was not surprised when the Albany *Knickerbocker News* commented that the legislators were "awed by their audacity" in advancing so much money for the advancement of the human spirit. They will be watching carefully to see how the money is specifically spent, said the paper. So will I.

Even before this emergency grant, New York was devoting twenty times as much money to the cause of the arts as California, our most populous state. New York is spending half as much as the federal government in the entire United States. Yet I did not hesitate. Without our orchestras, operas, theaters, and ballets, without our museums and libraries, without our community arts centers, without our performing artists, we would not be a society—only an economy. In this sense, I believe we are embarked in a larger quest for humanity.

Early in 1970 the Central Labor Council AFL-CIO initiated demonstration arts projects to test new ways of increasing participation by union members in cultural life. The City Center of Music and Drama in New York City initiated a two-week Celebration of the Arts for Children. The Touchstone Players and the National Theater of the Deaf developed new techniques for expressing words visually in terms of movement. The council's assistance helped meet the costs of a series of experimental performances of plays based on poetry for children with opportunity for dialogue between the performers and the young spectators.

We had a windfall when the Metropolitan Opera Association expressed an interest in donating its enormous backlog of costumes to a cultural development program. The council accepted, as a gift, costumes from fifteen Metropolitan Opera productions and stage settings from eight Metropolitan Opera national company productions. The council's grant covered consultants' fees, preliminary storage and shipping, inventory maintenance, insurance, and fund raising.

Since the mid-1960s the council has been actively concerned with broadening the appreciation of the work of contemporary writers. The list of an expanded poets' and writers' program of participating authors has grown to 50 writers of fiction, 25 playwrights, and 250 poets.

Mr. Al Craz, of Syosset, New York Public Schools, reported: "Syosset High School enjoyed three very rewarding visits from John Hollander, the poet. He inspired, illuminated, and challenged our students with reading his own poetry, reading the poetry of other fine poets, and discussing these poems. Already, students have requested that another poet be made available to the Teenage Coffee House in Syosset for discussions and more reading."

Mr. David Goff, a farmer with a deep love for rural crafts, is a prime mover in the Madison County Historical Society. Although he still gets up at 5 A.M. and goes to bed at 8 P.M., he has become an arts administrator with a state council grant. Mr. Goff now devotes full time to the Historical Society and rural crafts. He believes that every town in the United States has its hidden craftsmen, and if given the opportunity, they will be delighted to demonstrate their skills and show their wares to the community. Mr. Goff organizes the Crafts Fair at Oneida every September and thousands of visitors pour in. Now he is forming a regional Arts and Crafts Action Committee to further "the conservation of human resources."

During its ten-year history, the Council's Visual Arts Program concerned itself with the fine arts, architecture, photography, history, and science, serving as producer, consultant, and funding source. This variety of subject interests and functions gives the Visual Arts Program its unique character and permits its wide range of activity.

The New York State Legislature created the Museum Aid Program in 1966 in response to rapidly increasing museum audiences. "I liked it best because the things I saw were fun, even though I learned things," was one comment, expressing a universal sentiment, or so it seemed. In four years a total of 319 Museum Aid grants were made to 97 art, history, and science museums.

Late in 1967 Mr. Allon Schoener, Director of Visual Arts of the council, heard of an attempt to salvage and restore the area of southern Manhattan around the Fulton Fish Market. He visited the area and found Mr. Peter Stanford directing an enterprise that seemed at that time too big to be believed—the acquisition and restoration to early nineteenth-century appearance of the port area. Mr. Schoener immediately offered council assistance to establish a public program and recruit membership.

Now, at the beginning of 1970, the South Street Seaport has ten thousand members. It is one of New York's most exciting summer festivals. The state has authorized a Maritime Museum to be built there and the Seaport has acquired three old ships, including a three-masted square-rigger, the *Wavertree*.

Mr. Stanford, president of the South Street Seaport, said, "Council dollars are unusually hard-working dollars. This is due to the council's policy of providing advisory services and essential staff support. New institutions enable New Yorkers to participate in their cultural heritage. The social impact of this frontier work is evident."

The council has also been engaged in experiments directed toward art audience extension. In 1967, *Erie Canal: 1817–1967* served as a catalyst to activate canal communities to organize their own sesquicentennial celebrations. In 1969 the controversial *Harlem on My Mind: Cultural Capital of Black America, 1900–1968* attracted new urban audiences to the Metropolitan Museum of Art.

The State Council on the Arts advances technical assistance to communities and local groups—more than 170 regional projects this year. Recent applicants included a puppet theater that sought help with fund raising, an opera company that wanted improved stage directing, a black arts festival that needed program planning, an archeological excavation that wanted to film its activities, an urban renewal agency troubled with evaluation of historic buildings, and a group of architectural historians puzzled by the composition of old mortar.

Finally, in this area, we established the New York State Award for significant activities and accomplishments which enrich the quality of life of New York State residents. Among the thirteen recipients of the award from Lieutenant Governor Malcolm Wilson for 1969 were the Air Preheater Company of Wellsville, for pioneering support of the performing arts to provide a small upstate community with its first exposure to live arts events. The Brooklyn Academy of Music received an award for imaginative programing and the rehabilitation of one of the state's venerable theaters; the 92nd Street Young Men's and Young Women's Hebrew Association, New York City, for its sustained record of contribution to the arts, and the Xerox Corporation, Rochester, for its consistently courageous sponsorship of high quality and controversial network television programs.

The New York State Historic Trust is less elaborately funded than the State Council on the Arts. But I regard its mission, though perhaps less immediate, as equally profound. The Historic Trust operates and maintains thirty-nine historic sites. The attendance in a typical recent year was a phenomenal 523,000. This is expected to increase by 10 per cent in 1971.

The Historic Trust maintains the Battle Monument at Saratoga, on the site of the decisive victory over Burgoyne in the Revolutionary War. It also preserves the John Brown Farm at Lake Placid, where the abolitionist brooded and plotted for the overthrow of slavery in the southern states.

On top of a small hill known as Mount McGregor stands the cottage where General Ulysses S. Grant came to die. Knowing he had one year or so to live, the pain of cancer gripping his throat, he began to write his memoirs to provide a living for his family. Huddled on the porch, muffled in his shawl, Grant wrote one of the military classics of all time. The trust maintains the cottage today.

A greater writer, Walt Whitman, lived at Huntington, Long Island, and his home there is also maintained by our Historic Trust.

Not long ago, we established a state Nature and Historical Preserve Trust in the Conservation Department. The purpose is not only the preservation of wilderness areas located outside the Forest Preserve, but also the preservation of historic sites close to or within the state's metropolitan areas. Here the need for protection from development or destruction is the greatest. No limitation is placed on the size of any historic area or site. It may be a fraction of an acre or tens of thousands of acres.

This intense historical activity is designed not merely to re-create a quiet, stately, and authentic reminder of the past. Its purpose is to help orient us in the stream of history, to help remind us of the immense debt we owe to the past, and to strengthen our resolve to guard our heritage and enhance it for the generations to come. It is to help ensure that our future will hold the same opportunities worth remembering as our past.

The earth, as Jefferson said, belongs to the living. It should be shaped to their needs. But one of the needs of the living is for enduring values, rooted in history. Our programs enable us to come face to face with history and to appreciate our debt to it. Hopefully, they strengthen our resolve to create a future that will be worthy of it.

When John Hightower was recently appointed director of the Museum of Modern Art, he summed it up in these words:

"The healthiest aspect of government support of anything is the insistence with which it must consider the public . . . Public money requires that an arts organization perform a service for the public.

"Public money means that museums, symphony orchestras, opera companies will have to perform more than a curatorial function for a few connoisseurs, a handful of patrons, and the select members of the club. These will have to be contemporary for a much larger segment of society—to the benefit of both artist and audience."

GHETTO ARTS PROGRAM

Increasingly, we are emphasizing our Ghetto Arts Program. This provides artists in ghetto communities with the opportunity to develop their talent and present their work. It encourages activities that relate art to the everyday life of the ghetto. It aims at involving professional minority artists who recognize a stake in the communities in which they live.

The Afro-American Studio for Action and Speech provides the Harlem community with a planned curriculum for quality theater training and theatrical productions which emphasize Afro-American culture and history. Bed-Stuy Theater was created in 1969 as "a cultural-recreational facility with which residents of the Bedford-Stuyvesant community could identify." This group mounted a production of *Land Across the River* with state support.

The Bronx Council on the Arts sponsored two borough-wide summer programs in 1969–70. The Bronx Bandwagon was a bus-borne touring unit of fifty talented teenagers who entertained city-bound youngsters in day camps, play groups, and community centers in July and August. The Black Theater Workshop, composed of a group of drama students from Herbert H. Lehman College, presented weekly programs of dramatic readings of black literature, poetry, and plays.

The Brooklyn Academy of Music organized a summer program of free dance instruction supervised by Alvin Ailey. Over six hundred students between seven and twenty-five years of age attended the classes.

The Dance Theater of Harlem was created to break a

chain that all but excluded blacks from classic ballet. This organization comprises a school of dance and a dance company under the artistic direction of Arthur Mitchell. The dance company of sixteen professional black dancers performs in public schools and colleges throughout the state. At the school, which has 275 black students ranging in age from seven to forty, classic ballet, modern, ethnic, and jazz dance are taught with state council support.

Hospital Audiences, Inc., which has been serving the mental patients in twenty-four institutions for approximately three years, arranges for donated complimentary tickets. The Ghetto Arts Program also brings performers from the ghetto to state institutions to create a rapport and acquaint patients about to be released with the cultural facilities and performers in their communities.

The Lower East Side Civic Improvement Association's Tompkins Square Music Festival is an eagerly awaited event. In 1969–70 eleven free public concerts were held in Tompkins Square Park with gospel, jazz, folk, and protest music provided by musicians including Rafael Hernandez, Bernie Klay, the Fugs, and the Mellotones.

The Voice of Puerto Rico, under the joint sponsorship of the Puerto Rican Community Development Project, and the New York State Council on the Arts, presents a series of free cultural programs geared to New Yorkers of Puerto Rican descent. The Puerto Rican Traveling Theater Company, a professional bilingual, multiracial company, founded by the Puerto Rican actress Miriam Colón, has presented in Spanish Federico García Lorca's farce *Los Titeres de Cachiporra* at eight free matinee performances especially for children in public parks.

Summer on Wheels, directed by Chris White, continues to provide free performances for ghetto residents throughout the state and offers consultative services to communities with little access to trained professionals. Touring units include the Afro-American Folkloric Troupe, Al Fann Theatrical Ensemble, Alvin Ailey American Dance Theater, Movements Black, Movie Bus, Pickwick Puppet Theater, Soul and Latin Theater, Sounds Unlimited, and Young Film-makers Foundation.

Theater for the Forgotten, created in 1967, is designed to provide rehabilitation services and professional entertainment in prisons in New York. During the past year two plays, *The Brick and the Rose* and *Telemachus Clay*, were presented by inmates and professional actors at Riker's Island Prison. A touring show with professionals and inmate apprentices toured prisons in New York City, and workshops for released prisoners were also conducted at Riker's Island and Hart Island. More than fifty thousand inmates have seen the performances, and three hundred have participated in plays and workshops.

Finally the State Council on the Arts helps support the Urban Arts Corps. The Urban Arts Corps is no longer completely black but multiracial, and it uses the work of multinational playwrights, before white communities as well as black.

In 1969–70, its third year of activity and council support, the Corps gave performances of *But Never Jam Today* (an Afro-American musical adaptation of Lewis Carroll's *Alice in Wonderland*) as part of the Black Expo series at the City Center of Music and Drama in New York City. *Old Judge Mose Is Dead* and *Moon on a Rainbow Shawl* were presented by the Corps in Kingston, Newburgh, Albany, Syracuse, Rochester, Buffalo, and Geneva.

"To the extent we like ourselves, we are able to express the things that are us," said Vinette Carroll of the Urban Arts Corps, "but so many of our experiences are universal that I really think we're addressing other people, too."

Our struggle for the arts is part of our larger concern for that "inalienable right"—the pursuit of happiness. Man's environment is not only physical. It is of the mind, of the soul as well. Spiritual values may be less obvious than pure water or clean air—but man needs them too, if he truly is to live.

EIGHT

Do It—Now

In May 1970 I flew by helicopter into a rugged section of the new Hudson Highlands State Park on the Hudson's shores some forty miles from Manhattan. There, about two hundred people waited on a wooded promontory at the end of a dirt trail overlooking the majestic river. I talked with them for a while about the new 2500-acre state park, created by the joint efforts of private citizens, businessmen, and state government, stretching three miles or more through some of the most beautiful scenery on earth.

That late spring day in the Hudson Highlands, amid the sweep from Breakneck Ridge across the gorge to Stony Mountain, it seemed very clear to me that we were indeed on the verge of a decisive new phase in our struggle to save the environment. To date, we environmentalists have been fighting in the crusade launched by Gifford Pinchot and Theodore Roosevelt and others and extended by still others such as Fairfield Osborn and Rachel Carson. They proclaimed, and we in government have acted upon, the concept that conservation of our resources and their proper use is the fundamental problem that underlies almost every other problem of our national life.

Unless we maintain an adequate material basis for our civilization, as Pinchot and Roosevelt insisted, we cannot maintain the institutions in which we take so great and just a pride. To waste and destroy our natural resources means to undermine the material basis of our society, among much else. Yet hitherto as a nation, we tended to live with an eye "single to the present," and we permitted the reckless waste and destruction of much of our natural wealth.

Conservation means development as much as it does protection, the pioneers argued. Almost as a voice in the wilderness at his point in history, Theodore Roosevelt thundered, "I recognize the right and duty of this generation to develop and use our natural resources, but I do not recognize the right to waste them, or to rob the generations that come after us." It followed that the resources which are vital to the welfare of the whole people should be kept under the control of the whole people, held for the benefit of all our people, and not monopolized for the benefit of the few.

Now as then, of all the questions before the nation, there is none more significant than the task of leaving the planet a better place. This is a profound moral issue. Involved in it is the patriotic duty of insuring the safety and continuance of the nation and of what it means to all of the world.

By 1970 we have explored almost every square mile of this planet. We have begun to explore the lunar satellite and the more remote areas of the sea bed. We are planning a "grand tour" of the other planets, much in the mood of a photographic safari. We have explored the microcosm to the smallest subparticles of matter, split the atom, probed the secrets of chromosomes and genes and, through them, the key to life itself. "But with all our relentless searching for knowledge," as Ewald B. Nyquist, New York State Commissioner of Education, has put it, "we have forgotten that man himself is the ultimate reason for our eternal quest, and that the individual is still the basic unit of value in the human condition."

Since Gifford Pinchot and Theodore Roosevelt, the pace

of man's evolutionary journey has accelerated with unbelievable swiftness and many believe we have almost outrun ourselves. A part of us, the technological, has moved so far ahead of the rest of us, the ecological, that unless we pause to examine where we are going, and why, unless we harness our technology to serve our best interests and deepest instincts, we will not even come close to fulfilling our destiny.

Science, in the sense that it is pure thought, has been said to harm no one, and it need not be humanistic. But it is important to maintain a humanistic attitude toward technology —and to impose human controls upon it—if only in recognition of the harm technology can do.

Admiral Hyman Rickover developed the nuclear submarine which, in conjunction with the intercontinental missile, is a prime element in our peacekeeping deterrent strength. Admiral Rickover says: "Technology can have no legitimate purpose other than to serve man—man in general, not merely some men; future generations, not merely those who currently wish to gain advantage for themselves; man in the totality of his humanity, encompassing all his manifold interests and needs, not merely one particular concern of his.

"When viewed humanistically, technology is seen not as an end in itself, but as a means to an end, the end being determined by man himself in accordance with the laws prevailing in his society."

A NEW ENVIRONMENTAL ETHIC

In this spirit, I set forth for the 1970s the goal of the saving of our environment. Achievement of this goal will require the planning and the practical functioning of nothing less than a new environmental ethic. It will demand the participation of all of us. It will require the very clear reinterpretation of the Biblical conferring upon man of dominion over earth and over all living things. For every right, there is a responsibility, and for every opportunity, there exists an obligation. The new environmental ethic implies concern not only for human life, but for all life in the biosphere.

In recent testimony in Washington on the environment, Dr. J. George Harrar, president of The Rockefeller Foundation, said that "man's superior intelligence and his belief in the intrinsic worth of each human being do not entitle him to assume that the natural environment should be given over to the production and the maintenance of his own kind."

The new environmental ethic rests, moreover, on the assumption that technology alone may not provide the answers for all or even most of our ecological problems. For technology tends to the public demand—often stimulated by hard-sell advertising. As long as consumers expect goods to be produced at the lowest possible cost, in the largest possible quantity, at the greatest possible convenience, without regard to environmental consequences, then all the nature-loving rhetoric on earth is not going to save the earth.

We as citizens must, of necessity, adopt self-imposed restraints by which we will voluntarily refrain from contributing in greater degree to our ecological imbalance. We in industry, commerce, and agriculture must view ourselves not merely as producers and profit-makers but as citizens of the whole community—showing all the consideration and responsibility toward our neighbors that good citizenship demands. We in government have the responsibility to make these things happen if we are to leave our cities, our suburbs, and our countryside even a little better than we found it.

In July of 1970, New York State launched its new Department of Environmental Conservation. This will be the new unifying institution of our state in the new environmental crusade. Here we will plan and here we will achieve the ecological reforms of the 1970s.

We are bringing together into one department all the programs to enhance environmental quality—air, water, and land. We are encompassing the air and water pollution control programs and the solid waste programs that have been in the Department of Health. We are drawing in the forest management, fish and game conservation, public education and water resource management functions of the Department of Conservation. We are taking over pesticide controls from the Department of Agriculture and Markets.

I am also authorizing our new Department of Environmental Conservation to develop brand-new initiatives in many fields. We are at work on an overall environmental plan to bring the building blocks of a healthy land, clean air, and pure water into an ecological whole. To do this:

—We must assess social patterns and new technology so we can cope with emerging threats through measures which avert long-range adverse effects on the environment.

—We must foster and conduct research to gain the scientific and technological knowledge needed for more effective pollution control, and develop feasible ways to reuse and recycle wastes.

—We must initiate programs to combat excessive noise, pollution from spillages of oil and other materials in storage or transport, and other threats to the quality of our environment and the health and comfort of man.

The state legislature has established a new State Environmental Board to approve basic environmental standards of the state—i.e., air quality standards, thermal pollution standards, etc. This new streamlining organization will supersede the Water Resources Commission, the Air Pollution Control Board, the Pesticide Control Board, and the Natural Beauty Commission. It will bring together in one body the head of every state agency whose programs and policies have a major impact on the environment. It will help to evaluate program performance and ensure that it is consistent with state policy. It will also serve as a working forum for the exchange of ideas, the airing of emerging concerns and proposals relating to the environment.

I have named six voting members from private life to the board, to broaden perspectives and to offer fresh insights. They are Joe G. Moore, Jr., former Commissioner of the Federal Water Pollution Control Administration; Charles H. Callison, executive vice-president of the National Audubon Society; William H. Whyte, widely known authority on conservation law; Dr. Lamont C. Cole, world-renowned ecologist, author, lecturer, and professor of zoology at Cornell University; Dr. E. Corrine Brown Galvin, lecturer, author, teacher, and civic leader; and Jerome Wilkenfeld, a specialist in industrial pollution control.

We also established a Council of Environmental Advisors with seven members representing various environmental disciplines and the whole range of human concerns. The chairman is John L. Loeb, Jr., an investment banker, and members range from Arthur Godfrey, the entertainer and environmental crusader, to specialists in atmospheric and aquatic ecology. The council will develop guidelines to help us in assigning priorities, and will make independent reviews of key environmental issues.

For the other major prong of our environmental offensive, I have set in motion a new Office of Parks and Recreation, to become a department as soon as this is constitutionally possible. Parks and recreation are so important in my view that they must now become a separate, significant function of state government with independent identity and leadership.

The new Office of Parks and Recreation will seek to expand and diversify recreational opportunities for all of New York State's people. It will take steps to ensure the protection of natural resources located on state properties. It will plan, coordinate, and carry out recreational, parks, and historic preservation programs, and prepare a new state parks and recreation plan. It will stimulate the development of municipal and private parks and recreation programs, promote and regulate the recreational use of waterways by boaters, and carry out a special effort to provide recreation opportunities for residents of urban areas.

One of the instrumentalities of change, in my judgment, is already in hand. This is the very effective Pure Waters Authority, whose successes I have described earlier in this book. On July 1, 1970, therefore, with the approval of the legislature, I expanded the Pure Waters Authority into the New York State Environmental Facilities Corporation. The new corporation will be able to work, now, in all areas of environmental protection. It will be able to work in research, planning, testing, development, financing, construction, operation, and maintenance of all antipollution controls. It will meet the need of municipalities and other organizations for "a total package" of environmental services and facilities. The Environmental Facilities Corporation will also be authorized specifically to act as a "fire brigade" in emergency situations, such as rapid clean-ups of oil spills.

When I named Mr. Henry L. Diamond as the new Commissioner of Environmental Conservation, we drew in one of the new breed of dedicated, young environmental professionals who knows the urgency of the issues and will get things done. Mr. Diamond had been counsel to the President's Advisory Committee on Environmental Quality, a member of the Long Island State Park Commission and the President's Advisory Committee on Youth Opportunity. He served as director of the White House Conference on Natural Beauty. He was associated with Laurance S. Rockefeller for more than ten years.

A NEW ENVIRONMENTAL COALITION

Mr. Diamond got the new department off to a bustling start. "Diamond sparkled," the Albany *Times-Union* put it, unable to resist adding that he could become "an environmental gem." Mr. Diamond himself set forth his goals as involving the "formation of a new environmental coalition."

"We've got the tradition of leadership by the fish and wildlife people, the wilderness enthusiasts and sportsmen," he noted. "These people have always been interested and they have always provided the leadership. Now we have a new type of interested citizen. Maybe she is a mother who lives in the upper west side of New York City. She doesn't care anything about hunting or fishing and she doesn't really care about wilderness but she wants decent air for her child to breathe. She wants to look at the Hudson River and see it cleaned up as a place for her child to play.

"We are seeing a community of interest from the guy who might be a trout fisherman or a wilderness advocate and this mother in upper Manhattan formulating a whole new environmental coalition with a community of interest they didn't realize existed before. Basically, they are all seeking the same thing—healthy land, clean air, and pure water.

"There is great power here and, quite frankly, political clout to support pollution abatement programs, to support fish and wildlife programs, to support wilderness programs. I see this as a great opportunity to work together for the things we all want. So, it's not so much a redirection but a merging together of some interests that we didn't know were really communal."

By executive order, I have directed all elements of the state government to make findings of "ecological consequence" with the Department of Environmental Conservation before undertaking any major new projects of any kind.

As this was written in the summer of 1970, we were making plans to:

Open heretofore closed shellfish beds off Long Island and Westchester County because the Pure Waters program has now made them safe;

Authorize the removal of the first load of solid waste from Westchester County under a new contract with the Environmental Facilities Corporation;

Announce and demonstrate new state equipment to scoop up and dispose of oil spills;

Recommend to the legislature that we deposit new and ecologically valuable underwater state lands into new Historic Trusts so these will be preserved from sale or dredging;

Promote hearings on the strong pesticide controls now required by New York State, designed to instill a strict interpretation of the new laws;

Establish a training program for young environmentalists using a volunteer system tried and proven in the education of foresters and in the development of safety measures for hunters;

Open industrial pollution control facilities, such as those installed by Eastman Kodak in Rochester or Republic Steel in Buffalo, and also to open new municipal waste treatment plants in towns such as Oswego;

Contract for detergent products with biodegradable characteristics and research the market for products to lessen the pollution of our streams;

Place contracts wherever possible for electric or propane gas fork lift trucks in place of those operated by gasoline;

Develop a telecommunications system for continuous reporting to a central location on the pollutants in the water and in the atmosphere—some automatic monitors already are in service;

Persuade more banks and other financial institutions to make low cost loans to business and municipalities for pollution control facilities;

Initiate a new state urban forestry program to help cities save their trees and plant new ones;

Hold hearings and set up the list of endangered species of wildlife that will be protected under new state laws;

Begin the pilot operation of the new state environmental services to towns, counties, and villages authorized, but not funded, in the current budget;

Open Rockland Lake Park South, another new state park specifically designed to provide urban recreation opportunities.

Whenever the new Environmental Conservation Department wishes to act on a major pollution problem, we will have the powers to take corrective action, including summary abatement powers. "This means we can go in and say, 'Stop what you're doing,'" said Commissioner Diamond. "And we'll litigate about it later."

But we are rather less concerned with powers than we are with public education and acceptance. We seek cooperation, not confrontation. We are planning to set up environmental councils everywhere in the state, at the city and county level. We are developing an environmental education study program for all of our public schools. We frankly hope to create an educational "package" that will be extremely attractive and geared to the possibilities of a higher quality of life.

EARTH DAY 1970—A BEGINNING

On Earth Day, April 22, 1970, early in the morning, I went to the legislature in Albany with Senate Majority Leader Earl W. Brydges, Senator Bernard C. Smith, and Assemblyman Glen Harris. We met more than seven hundred student leaders from throughout the state, and I signed into law the new Department of Environmental Conservation. That morning, incidentally, I proved that I could still ride a bicycle—even though I was so preoccupied with staying on the thing that I rode the wrong way on a one-way street.

Traveling to New York City that same day, we attended a marvelous rally in Prospect Park, Brooklyn, sponsored by a number of Brooklyn schools and community groups. Then we went to Manhattan by subway to join the enormous Earth Day rally on Fourteenth Street where there was no room to ride a bicycle. I visited our state exhibits at the Earth Day rally. There was a tank car filled with really pure water, brought down from the Catskill Mountains; an artistic montage of garbage cans and the like contributed by the State Council on the Arts; and a state bandstand where teenagers were bouncing up and down "declaring war"—as one rock singer put it—against the pollution of our environment.

State agency assistance was offered and accepted by students throughout the state for Earth Day, and we responded to nearly two thousand inquiries. More than 320 state officials spoke around the state about pollution. We distributed buttons and posters in support of Earth Day to 180 colleges and 55 high schools and we loaned out all 178 prints of our films on environmental subjects to students. Finally, we sent out about 25,000 anti-litter kits to 5000 elementary schools across the state, suggesting they be used in the Earth Day observance.

The Earth Day Teach-Ins generated new ideas, new thinking, and new action to rescue our environment, to awaken our nation, and to turn us toward environmental salvation before it is too late. That the leadership was undertaken by our younger generation is one of the most positive signs I have seen in a long time. It is a healthy omen for the future.

Earth Day will not signal an end, but, hopefully, the beginning of a new regard for the life-giving balance between man and his environment. I therefore propose that Earth Day be henceforth celebrated every year, everywhere in the United States, on April 22.

"It's a beautiful thing," said Mr. Jeff Tarber, of the Boston University Law School's Environmental Society about Earth Day. "It brings together radicals and members of the John Birch Society. It seems to be a meeting ground." Mr. Peter Maule, of Ecology Action at San Francisco State, said, "People will have to realize that if we are to survive, we are going to have to change our life style, and modes of consumption." The Albany *Times-Union* said, "Nobody can seriously come out against a clean environment."

Public opinion is continuing to move very rapidly in favor of increased environmental planning and antipollution controls. In August 1965 a Harris Poll asked its respondents, "As an American, have you often, sometimes, or hardly ever felt bad because of the pollution of rivers and streams." Forty-three per cent felt concerned, and 57 per cent said "hardly ever." In July 1967 another Harris Poll showed that 72 per cent of the people in the cities and 75 per cent in the suburbs felt there was a great deal of air pollution in their neighborhoods. But only 44 per cent were willing to pay $15 in additional taxes each year to finance a federal air-pollution campaign.

With the *priorities* of federal spending the issue in 1970, the Harris Poll went back to document the new public attitude toward the environment. The respondents were asked which area of government spending they would most like to see cut, and which they would least like to see cut. Only 3 per cent said cut most for pollution control, and 55 per cent said cut least. Pollution control was the second most popular issue nationwide, by this measurement, second only to federal aid to education. On the other hand, 66 per cent of the respondents said cut first on foreign aid. The respondents also favored cuts in spending in Vietnam and in the space program.

Edmund K. Faltermayer, in his comprehensive *Redoing America*, asked:

"Why are we settling for less than a massive rollback of pollution, as a near-term objective? One reason is that the public, for all its growing concern, is unaware that most of the techniques for drastically lowering pollution already exist or could be developed within a few years. The other reason is that some industrial spokesmen have bandied about vague but frighteningly large figures implying that a real clean-up would virtually bankrupt the economy."

Actually, most of the evidence shows that cleaning up pollution will save money and will enhance the prosperity of the country. As for advancing technology, I have described a little of it in this book, and it is impressive indeed. The federal government estimates the losses caused by atmospheric and water pollution exceed $25 billion each year.

The government estimates property damage caused by pollution to add another $12 billion per year to the bill. These costs do not include the unnatural depressing of real estate values in districts with second-class air and water supplies, or close to noisy factories or airports. For example, the annual amount of sulfur dioxide vented into the air, one of our worst pollutants, is itself worth some $300 million and all of it is lost.

"To save the United States from becoming a malodorous wasteland," said *Time* magazine, after synthesizing the best governmental and industrial cost estimates, "will cost nearly $100 billion in the next five years." This is $20 billion per year, or roughly one fourth of the defense budget. Put another way, the bill is roughly $100 per person per year.

WE "CAN" AFFORD IT

Once priorities are set, the targets become less costly to attain. *Time*'s synthesis showed that the $700 million annual cost of curbing industrial and power plant pollution would add between twenty and thirty cents to most consumers' monthly electric bills. *Time* commented, "However unpopular such extra tariffs might be, the price is modest if it will buy the fresh and clean water that is fast becoming only a memory in the United States."

I am wary about empirical cost accounting, but the overall point is well taken: Not only *can* our environment be saved; the saving of the environment *can* be financed.

This brings us back again to the complex but critical problem of planning and organization bedeviling us all. Until very recently, there were ninety separate environmental programs in the federal government. There were twenty-six quasi-governmental bodies and fourteen interagency committees at work in and out of Washington on the problems. The *Reader's Digest* commented, "We are managing our resources like a department store. We have appointed dozens of managers for the individual departments but nobody is watching the store as a whole. The result is a chain of narrow interest decisions that block any overall look at what we are doing to the land."

The United States Interior Department's Park Service has long had an interest in lobbying chambers of commerce to try to infringe upon the Department of Agriculture's Forest Service, since forest land does not bring in as much tourist business as parkland. The Soil Conservation Service of the Agriculture Department competes with the Army Corps of Engineers and the Interior Department's Bureau of Reclamation over who can protect watersheds most effectively. The Tennessee Valley Authority, famed worldwide as the classic dispenser of cheap electricity, obtains approximately half of the coal it needs for its power plants from the very stripmining companies that are wrecking much of Kentucky and other states.

On this subject the *Reader's Digest* is bitterly and constructively critical:

"Behind the FPC are the advocates of private power; behind Reclamation and TVA are the public power supporters. Behind the state road departments are the trucking, road-building, and gas and oil lobbies. Behind the U. S. Army Corps of Engineers is the most powerful lobby of all—the huge dam and harbor-building contractors. The need for action grows daily. For unless we stop managing our resources in the present fragmented way, we will soon run out of things worth fighting to keep."

This is why I set up our new State Department of Environmental Conservation. It is why New York City set up its own comprehensive environmental department at the municipal level. And that is why the federal government has followed suit with its new Environmental Protection Agency.

A WORLDWIDE EFFORT

The United States also has a fine opportunity to help coordinate international planning for environmental controls. The proposed United Nations Conference on the Environment, to be held in Stockholm in 1972, can be a major forward step toward a better environment. As a pioneer in the national park concept and in the concern for environmental quality, the United States has much to contribute to the conference. We also have much to learn from what other nations are doing to solve their own pollution problems.

Much as the environment is a unifying issue within the United States, it can become an area of increased cooperation between nations. The resolution suggesting the conference was introduced by Sweden and attracted fifty-one co-sponsors including the United States. The Soviet Union supported the idea during the floor debate. I therefore recommend that the preparation for U.S. participation be given a high priority. I further recommend that United States citizen organizations, business leaders, and environmental authorities be given an opportunity to play an important role in the conference. We might even make Earth Day earthwide.

A vital development in this regard is taking place within the North Atlantic Treaty Organization. NATO is moving into the field of environmental protection under the rather general authority of its Article II, which calls for the promotion of international stability and well being. In December 1969 the first meeting was held of a new NATO Committee on the Challenges of Modern Society. The Committee recommended that seven NATO pilot studies be conducted under the sponsorship of individual countries for the benefit of all the member nations. For example, Road safety—the United States; Open waters pollution—Belgium; Individual fulfillment in an industrial society—Britain; Transmission of scientific knowledge to decision-making sectors of government—West Germany.

NATO Secretary-General Manlio Brosio reaffirmed that military defense and political activity would continue to be first NATO functions. But—and here is the mood of the

1970s: "However, the reconciliation of modern man with his environment is an increasingly urgent and necessary task in our society. Our efforts will not be directed toward research, but toward questions of government policy formulation, and legislation, ways and means of action to bring about improvements in our physical and social environment."

In the research field, an International Biological Program, involving fifty-seven nations, is conducting some fascinating ecological studies which should do much to ensure the success of the United Nations Conference on the Environment. The United States is contributing $4 million to this program in 1970, incidentally, and it will increase its investment to $7 million in 1971.

One United States survey has mobilized eighty scientists in four hundred counties between the Mississippi and the Rocky Mountains. The scientists are tracking down basic knowledge about the ecology of the prairies—trailing antelope and noting the interaction of cattle and lark buntings that nest on saltbush plants that cows like to nibble. In Brazil international scientists are listing the "lessons" that advanced people can learn from Indians in community behavior, while also studying the Amazon rain forest, one of the world's principal suppliers of oxygen. In India the biologists are studying human and animal life at high altitudes, where more people in time theoretically might want to live, as they now throng to the coasts.

Mr. George F. Kennan, who has proposed an International Environment Agency, said, "For young people the world over, some new opening of hope and creativity is becoming an urgent spiritual necessity. Could there, one wonders, be any undertaking better designed to meet these needs, to relieve the great convulsions of anxiety and ingrained hostility that now rack international society, than a major international effort to restore the hope, the beauty, the salubriousness of the natural environment in which man has his being."

What can the individual citizen do? Here is an Earth Day type of checklist—a rundown of ideas that might be useful:

1. Educate yourself about ecological principles, the interdependence of all living things with their environment. Aware of the fragile balance of these forces, you can better convince others of the threat to the life cycle.

2. Take a local pollution inventory. Attend the city council meetings and antipollution hearings. Insist that existing antipollution laws be strictly enforced.

3. Become familiar with pending antipollution bills or ordinances. Inaugurate letter-writing campaigns or petitions to industrialists, mayor, governor, congressman, or senators.

4. Speeches, seminars, panel discussions. Go to your community for speakers—conservation clubs, university faculty, graduate students, local and state public officials, biology, science teachers from other schools, district soil conservationist, game manager, forester.

5. Invite representatives from local polluters to address your group. *Get the facts* beforehand; then use the question and answer period to find out how they plan to mend their ways.

6. Curricula development—perhaps the most important goal you can seek. Environmental understandings and reverence must be taught from kindergarten on to ensure that future generations treat the earth with more respect than the present population has.

7. Encourage all teachers to bring environment into their lesson plans. Start ecology clubs in schools.

8. High school students prepare ecology speeches and presentations for elementary grades.

9. Make a Declaration of Environmental *Inter*dependence or Environmental Bill of Rights.

10. Environmental themes, term papers, science projects; chemistry students measure pollutants in air and water; ecology essay; poetry contest.

11. Make posters or banners for school walls and commercial establishments.

12. Establish an environmental corner in the library—books, clippings from newspapers and magazines, pictures; ecology bulletin board.

13. Articles or themes in school or community paper. Start your own newsletter.

14. Raise money for radio "spots," newspaper ads. Discuss environment on "talk" shows.

15. Distribute reprints of good newspaper and magazine articles.

16. Make your own antipollution film or slide presentation accompanied by music. Rock and folk music are often very effective.

17. Write antipollution skits or songs. Sell buttons and bumper stickers.

18. Field trips: Polluted areas, industry, examples of model pollution control, ecology hikes; tree-planting project.

19. Visit your community's sewage disposal and water treatment plants.

20. Publicize trash clean-up; scavenger hunt for polluting objects; clean-up section of a creek or mile of highway; centrally located heap of nonreturnable bottles; massive nonbuying of nonreturnable bottles.

21. Environmental hotline: Telephone number through which environmental information can be obtained and volunteers enlisted.

22. Environmental booths in business section—hand out antipollution leaflets, articles, litter bags, sell buttons and bumper stickers, have people sign petitions.

23. Ecology fair: Photographic displays, exhibits, posters, water samples, bottled "clean air," sculpture

made from trash or waste products, special "post office" for depositing letters to governmental and industrial officials regarding environmental problems.

24. Conduct pollution attitude survey—a great way to make people think; door-to-door, street corners, grocery stores, from environmental booths.

25. Obliterate the so-called generation gap—people of all ages to participate in environmental crusade.

26. Work to elect political candidates who favor strong antipollution legislation.

For those men and women who live on the land outside our cities, here is another checklist which will contribute to wildlife protection and increase enjoyment of the natural world in which we live:

1. In backyards, provide shelter boxes for squirrels, bird feeders for birds, bird baths with dripping water, turtle pools, wildlife fruit-bearing trees and shrubs, bird nesting boxes, clumps of sunflower plants, suet holders, sugar water vials for hummingbirds, stone fences without concrete for chipmunks.

2. In parklands and city open lands, help provide suitable travel lanes and shelter clumps and fencerows for song and game birds.

3. Leave some dead trees for woodpeckers, squirrels, owls.

4. Mow meadows only after nesting season.

5. Encourage tall grass around trees, rocks, water edges.

6. Allow some open land to lie fallow; plow twenty-foot strips on three- and four-year rotation; different strips will produce different plants, attract insects, and other organisms, birds, mammals.

7. Construct waterholes, ponds, and lakes wherever possible; follow a professionally prepared wildlife plan.

8. Keep one or two ponds open in the winter (quarter to half acre openings) for ducks and geese.

9. Let streams, rivers, sloughs, shorefronts develop natural niches, save or restore a bit of bog, swamp, marsh or prairie.

10. In the suburbs, develop a bluebird trail, help set up a private or public wildlife sanctuary.

11. Favor trees and shrubs with food and shelter value for wildlife, such as mountain ash, autumn olive, black cherry, hawthorne, crab-apple, apple trees, beech, oaks, hickories, butternut, maple, birch, hemlock, white pine.

12. Build a farm pond—help is available from the U. S. Soil Conservation Service.

13. Encourage your suburb to acquire open land, keep open space in forests, agriculture.

14. Help schools, churches, museums, hospitals make their grounds attractive to wildlife.

My brother Laurance S. Rockefeller is chairman of the Citizens Advisory Committee on Environmental Quality in Washington. In the appendix to this book, I add his list of addresses and telephone numbers of federal and state offices concerned with environmental problems and complaints. I include his committee's list of some organizations in the field. I also append his committee's idea of useful books about the environment.

In New York State we are proving we *can* save our environment—and we rejoice that our citizens are keeping up the pressure. Not long ago at the City Hall in Watertown, youth delegations from Watertown High School and Immaculate Heart Central School met to discuss environmental control with the whole council. The Watertown *Times* was there to report the courteous blow-by-blow.

The high school students set the mood by bringing into City Hall some plastic bags filled with refuse, samples of polluted water from Black River and Kelsey Creek, and photographs of polluted locations in the vicinity of Watertown.

The councilmen told the high school students that the city has a weekly trash-garbage collection, operates a $7,000,000 sewage disposal plant and interceptor sewer system, runs an extensive landfill operation for municipal refuse and garbage disposal, has a smoke pollution ordinance and an anti-littering ordinance.

"The city spends many thousands of dollars annually for pollution control," said Mayor Theodore Rand. He added that he had seen too many students throwing trash about the streets lately. Would more trashcans help? the students asked. The mayor said he doubted it. Mr. Ronald G. Forbes, the city manager, said there were already three hundred in town.

The students asked whether the city had planned ahead in the jet age against increased air pollution. The mayor said the number of jets in use now presented "no problem," but it would be difficult to determine whom to see about that problem.

One youngster, Robert Londraville, said there had been a great deal of talk about a new Ecological Commission for Watertown and he asked if youth could be represented on it. Another student, Kathy Russell, asked, "What good are laws if they aren't enforced?"

At this point, Peter Austin, another student, asked whether Watertown city officials had to bring pressure to bear upon local industries to obtain compliance with anti-pollution ordinances. The city manager said that "only today" the New York Air Brake Company had entered the municipal sewage and industrial waste disposal program, and this was a considerable step forward for the whole community.

It is exciting—and profoundly significant—that our young people are so interested and so active in this field.

They recognize the roots of the present environmental crisis. The real challenge is what we are all going to do about them.

The idea of turning back the clock to a simpler time may have some sentimental appeal, but it is just not practical. We obviously are not going to bury the automobile, as a group of California students did, symbolically, but surely we are going to have to produce a cleaner-burning engine.

We are not going to give up electric lighting, electron microscopes, heart and lung machines, and modern industry. But we do expect cleanly produced electric power to run them.

We are not going to be able to live without bottles and containers for our foods and materials, but we can improve them and make them reusable so that they do not defile our landscape.

We are not going to return to an era that lacked the labor-saving devices and the health-enhancing equipment of the modern kitchen or bathroom, nor back to a culture that was denied the vistas and enjoyment contributed by the radio, record player, and television set. But what we can do is to minimize their "instant obsolescence" and develop a system for recycling and reusing the raw materials—ever scarcer and more expensive—from which they are made.

We are not going back to a time before pesticides, when almost a third of our crops were lost to insects and disease. But we need to know more about the long-term effects of these chemicals.

We are going to have to mediate the competing claims of the economy and the environment, and resolve them sensibly in the interest of the whole man, not simply economic man—not just for today, but for posterity.

We *can* save our environment—and we shall save it because we must.

APPENDIX I

Federal and State Agencies
in the Environmental Field

BUREAU OF OUTDOOR RECREATION
Department of the Interior, Washington, D.C. 20240

The Bureau coordinates federal recreation programs and administers matching grants to states for state and local outdoor recreation planning, land acquisition and development projects.

Regional Offices

NORTHEAST:
> 1421 Cherry Street
> Philadelphia, Pa. 19102

SOUTHEAST:
> 810 New Walton Building
> Atlanta, Ga. 30303

LAKE CENTRAL:
> 3853 Research Park Drive
> Ann Arbor, Mich. 48104

MID CONTINENT:
Denver Federal Center, Bldg. 41
Denver, Colo. 80225

PACIFIC NORTHWEST:
U. S. Courthouse, Room 407
Seattle, Wash. 98104

PACIFIC SOUTHWEST:
450 Golden Gate Avenue, Box 36062
San Francisco, Cal. 94102

FEDERAL WATER POLLUTION
CONTROL ADMINISTRATION

Department of the Interior, 633 Indiana Avenue, N.W., Washington, D.C. 20240. It makes grants for comprehensive river basin planning, for the construction of waste treatment work, and for research, development, and demonstration projects.

Regional Offices

NORTHEAST REGION (Conn., Del., Me., Mass., N.H., N.J., N.Y., R.I., Vt.)
John F. Kennedy Building, Room 2303
Boston, Mass. 02203

MIDDLE ATLANTIC REGION (D.C., Md., N.C., Pa., S.C., Va.)
918 Emmet Street
Charlottesville, Va. 22901

SOUTHEAST REGION (Ala., Fla., Ga., Miss., P.R., Tenn., Virgin Islands)
1421 Peachtree Street, N.E., Suite 300
Atlanta, Ga. 30309

SOUTH CENTRAL REGION (Ark., La., N.M., Okla., Tex.)
1402 Elm Street
Dallas, Tex. 75202

OHIO BASIN REGION (Ind., Ky., O., W. Va.)
4676 Columbia Parkway
Cincinnati, O.   45226

GREAT LAKES REGION (Ill., Ia., Mich., Minn., Wisc.)
33 East Congress Parkway, Room 410
Chicago, Illinois   60605

MISSOURI BASIN REGION (Colo., Kan., Mo., Nebr., N.D., S.D., Wyo.)
911 Walnut Street, Room 702
Kansas City, Mo.   64106

SOUTHWEST REGION (Ariz., Calif., Hawaii, Nev., Utah, Guam)
760 Market Street
San Francisco, Calif.   94102

NORTHWEST REGION (Alaska, Idaho, Mont., Ore., Wash.)
Room 570, Pittock Block
Portland, Ore.   97205

THE DEPARTMENT OF AGRICULTURE

Washington, D.C.   20250. Its many agencies have become increasingly involved in programs for recreation and landscape conservation, and in urban as well as rural areas.

The department has a field man for one or more of its agencies in every county, and you should go to him to find out more about the various programs. Agencies will be listed in phone directories under U. S. Government—Agriculture, or County Extension Agent.

DEPARTMENT OF HEALTH, EDUCATION AND WELFARE

Washington, D.C.   20201. The Office of Education provides Title III grants and services for environmental education programs, facilities, and materials. The Public Health Service provides research, training, technical assistance, and grants-in-aid for air pollution and solid waste control.

Regional Offices

REGION I: (Conn., Me., Mass., N.H., R.I., Vt.)
John F. Kennedy Federal Building
Government Center
Boston, Mass.   02203

REGION II: (N.H., N.Y., P.R., Virgin Islands)
Federal Building
26 Federal Plaza
New York, N.Y.   10007

REGION III: (Pa., Del., Md., D.C., Va., W. Va.)
220 Seventh Street, N.E.
Charlottesville, Va.

REGION IV: (N.C., S.C., Ky., Tenn., Miss., Ala., Ga., Fla.)
50 Seventh Street, N.E.
Atlanta, Ga.   30323

REGION V: (Ill., Ind., Mich., Minn., O., Wisc.)
433 West Van Buren Street
Chicago, Ill.   60607

REGION VI: (Ark., La., N.M., Okla., Tex.)
1114 Commerce Street
Dallas, Tex.

REGION VII: (Ia., Kan., Mo., Neb.)
601 East 12th Street
Kansas City, Mo.   64106

DEPARTMENT OF HOUSING AND URBAN DEVELOPMENT
Washington, D.C.   20410. It provides grants in metropolitan
areas to expand community beautification programs, to help
state and local governments acquire open space, prepare comprehensive local, regional, or statewide plans.

Regional Offices

REGION I: (Conn., Me., Mass., N.Y., N.H., R.I., Vt.)
26 Federal Plaza
New York, N.Y. 10007

REGION II: (Del., D.C., Md., N.J., Pa., Va., W. Va.)
6th & Walnut Streets
Philadelphia, Pa. 19106

REGION III: (Ala., Fla., Ga., Ky., Miss., N.C., S.C., Tenn.)
645 Peachtree-Seventh Building
Atlanta, Ga. 30323

REGION IV: (Ill., Ind., Ia., Mich., Minn., Neb., N.D., O., S.D., Wisc.)
360 N. Michigan Avenue, Room 1500
Chicago, Ill. 60601

REGION V: (Ark., Colo., Kan., La., Mo., N.M., Okla., Tex.)
819 Taylor Street
Fort Worth, Texas 76102

REGION VI: (Ariz., Calif., Guam, Hawaii, Nev., Southern Idaho, Utah, Wyo.)
450 Golden Gate Avenue
San Francisco, Calif. 94102

(Alaska, Mont., Northern Idaho, Ore., Wash.)
Area Office: 2nd & Union
Seattle, Wash. 98101

REGION VII: (P.R. and the Virgin Islands)
P.O. Box 3869
GOP San Juan, P.R. 00936

STATE AGENCIES

The names of the agencies vary from state to state; in one, for example, the principal conservation agency might be called the Department of Natural Resources; in another, the Conservation Commission. However, if you write to the Department of Conservation and Natural Resources, State Capital, your letter will probably find its way to the right office. Similarly, a letter directed to the Department of Parks and Recreation will reach the principal recreation agency, whatever its precise title. State planning agencies can be key contacts.

In New York, write to The Department of Environmental Conservation, Albany, New York 12206.

Most state agencies have local offices in the principal cities, and for a condensed list of their names, addresses, and phone numbers, use the phone directory. Under the main listing for the state will be a list of the principal agencies.

The State University is another source of help. Increasingly, state universities are doing advisory and research work in environmental resource problems. Virtually every State University has an agricultural extension service, and many have services for urban problems.

APPENDIX II

Private Organizations

Most of the organizations listed here provide informational and publication services and a number have staff people to lend guidance to local groups. Many of these organizations have branches or charters in the states and cities. For a more complete listing of organizations in the conservation fields, you should consult the "Conservation Directory." This is published annually by the National Wildlife Federation, 1412 16th Street, N.W., Washington, D.C. 20036: $1.50 a copy. It is a useful guide for finding allies.

THE CONSERVATION FOUNDATION, 1250 Connecticut Avenue, N.W., Washington, D.C. 20036. Through research the foundation seeks to further knowledge about the interaction between man and nature; it also seeks to have this knowledge applied to the practical problems of urban growth, such as river basin planning, highway design, and regional development policies. It serves as a clearing house on information about significant new legislation and governmental programs, help for better conservation education in our schools, and has an extensive audiovisual and publications program.

THE GARDEN CLUB OF AMERICA, 598 Madison Avenue, New York, New York 10022. A national organization representing numerous local garden clubs. Active at the local level in beautification, conservation, and open space planning. Distributes a free conservation packet, "The World Around You."

GENERAL FEDERATION OF WOMEN'S CLUBS, 1734 N Street, N.W., Washington, D.C. 20036. Unites and serves affiliated local clubs. Its biennial Community Improvement Program offers incentive awards to clubs for outstanding projects to meet local needs, including outdoor recreation needs. Its Conservation Department assists clubs with conservation and outdoor recreation projects.

THE IZAAK WALTON LEAGUE OF AMERICA, 1326 Waukegan Road, Glenview, Illinois 60025. A membership organization with local chapters and state divisions; also national memberships. Promotes conservation of renewable natural resources and development and protection of high quality outdoor recreation opportunities. Chapters and divisions can furnish speakers and literature. Publishes monthly *Izaak Walton Magazine*. Maintains a Conservation Office at 719 13th Street, N.W., Washington, D.C. 20005.

KEEP AMERICA BEAUTIFUL, INC., 99 Park Avenue, New York, New York 10016. A national nonprofit, public service organization for the prevention of litter and for the enhancement of urban and rural scenic and man-made beauty. Publishes helpful brochures and newsletters on litter prevention.

LEAGUE OF WOMEN VOTERS OF THE UNITED STATES, 1730 M Street, N.W., Washington, D.C. 20036. A membership organization, with local and state leagues, dedicated "to promote political responsibility through informed and active participation of citizens in government." Members participate in water resource programs at all levels of government. Many local and state leagues are interested in open space, parks, and outdoor recreation facilities. Its national office can assist local leagues in study and action programs.

NATIONAL ASSOCIATION OF COUNTIES, Suite 522, 1001 Connecticut Avenue, N.W., Washington, D.C. 20036. A national, nonprofit membership organization which acts as a clearing house for information relating specifically to county government administration. Publishes a variety of materials relating to parks, air pollution, water pollution, etc.

NATIONAL ASSOCIATION OF SOIL AND WATER CONSERVATION DISTRICTS, 1025 Vermont Avenue, N.W., Washington, D.C. 20005. A membership organization of local districts and their state associations through which farmers and other landowners express their views on "judicious use of land, water, timber, and related resources." Its Recreation and Wildlife Committee and local districts can advise landowners considering income-producing recreational enterprises.

NATIONAL AUDUBON SOCIETY, 1130 Fifth Avenue, New York, New York, 10028. A membership organization dedicated to the conservation of wildlife and the natural environment. It has 150 local chapters; operates 40 wildlife sanctuaries across the country. It provides a wide variety of teaching aids to introduce school children to nature study. Its Nature Centers Division has provided guidance in planning and operating community nature centers. Intensive summer programs at four Audubon Camps offer adult courses in ecology for teachers and youth leaders. Publishes two bimonthlies, *Audubon* magazine and *Audubon Field Notes*.

NATIONAL COUNCIL OF STATE GARDEN CLUBS, 4401 Magnolia Avenue, St. Louis, Missouri 63110. The state clubs conduct a variety of programs for the beautification of the countryside and the cities. They also sponsor adult education courses in landscape principles and techniques.

NATIONAL RECREATION AND PARK ASSOCIATION, 1700 Pennsylvania Avenue, N.W., Washington, D.C. 20006. A national membership service organization active in the fields of recreation and park development, conservation, and beautification. It has a community service department, publishes many helpful booklets and a monthly magazine, *Parks and Recreation*.

NATIONAL TRUST FOR HISTORIC PRESERVATION, 748 Jackson Place, N.W., Washington, D.C. 20006. Semipublic agency set up to preserve historic properties of national significance and to encourage local preservation efforts. Publishes a quarterly magazine, *Historic Preservation*, and a monthly newspaper, *Preservation News*.

NATIONAL WILDLIFE FEDERATION, 1412 16th Street, N.W., Washington, D.C. 20036. Seeks to encourage citizen and governmental action for the conservation of natural resources. Publishes The Conservation Directory annually at $1.50 a copy.

NATURAL SCIENCE FOR YOUTH FOUNDATION, 763 Silvermine Road, New Canaan, Connecticut 06840. Helps communities set up natural science centers, wildlife preserves, and trailside museums for involving young people first hand with the world of nature.

THE NATURE CONSERVANCY, 1522 K Street, N.W., Washington, D.C. 20005. A membership organization with state chapters. It seeks to preserve natural areas by direct acquisition and by assistance to educational institutions, private groups, or public agencies. Through its revolving fund it often secures endangered property and holds it for later resale to public agencies.

OPEN SPACE INSTITUTE, 145 E. 52nd Street, New York, New York 10022. Action group which stimulates open space conservation by working with landowners, municipal agencies, civic and regional groups. Has excellent publication program.

ROADSIDE COUNCILS. In a number of states, Roadside Councils have been set up to work for highway billboard controls, scenic highways, and roadside rests. There is, unhappily, no national organization, but the California Roadside Council serves as a clearing house for state councils. It is located at 2636 Ocean Drive, San Francisco, California 94132.

SEARS, ROEBUCK FOUNDATION, Chicago, Illinois 60607. Sears has an extensive program for stimulating local action for conservation and beautification; through the Women's Clubs it gives grants to groups for pace-setting projects and each year awards prizes for outstanding accomplishment.

SIERRA CLUB, 1050 Mills Tower, San Francisco, California 94104. Devoted to study and protection of the nation's scenic resources—mountains, shorelines, parks, waters, forests, wildlife. It provides films, manuals, exhibits, speakers; sponsors conferences. Its quality book publishing program is unique in conservation.

THE URBAN COALITION, 2100 M Street, N.W., Washington, D.C. 20037. A nonprofit organization aimed at spurring people and groups to join together in action on the major problems of their cities.

URBAN LAND INSTITUTE, 1200 18th Street, N.W., Washington, D.C. 20036. An organization of commercial developers and others interested in planning and development of urban areas. Outstanding for its hard-headed studies of land use patterns.

YOUNG WOMEN'S CHRISTIAN ASSOCIATION, National Board, 600 Lexington Avenue, New York, New York 10022. Long noted for its work in training young people in the appreciation and use of our outdoor resources, it is also becoming increasingly active in stimulating community planning and beautification efforts through its local chapters. It has an excellent publications program.

APPENDIX III

Some Useful Publications

Clean Water—It's Up to You: A citizen's guide to clean water action. 48 p. Available free from the Izaak Walton League, 1326 Waukegan Road, Glenview, Illinois 60025.

The Big Water Fight: By the League of Women Voters' Education Fund. An informative discussion of citizen action on problems of water supply, pollution, floods, and planning. 1966. 246 p. $6.95 a copy. Available from the Stephen Greene Press, Brattleboro, Vermont.

Catalog of Federal Domestic Assistance: A definitive listing and explanation of all federal assistance programs. Available free from the Information Center, Office of Economic Opportunity, Executive Office of the President, Washington, D.C. 20506.

Challenge of the Land: Fine reference book for municipal officials and civic leaders on action to save open space. By Charles E. Little. 1968. 151 p. $3.75. Available from the Open Space Institute, 145 E. 52nd Street, New York, New York 10022.

Cluster Development: Comprehensive report on how better subdivision planning can provide more open space. 1964. 138 p.

Illustrated. By William H. Whyte. $3.00 soft cover, $6.00 hard cover. Published by American Conservation Association, 30 Rockefeller Plaza, New York, New York 10020.

Community Action Program for Water Pollution Control: Community Action Program for Air Pollution Control: Two highly recommended books which discuss the problems of organization, enabling legislation, enforcement, staffing, financial and technical assistance, and how to drum up community support. $1.00 each. Available from the National Association of Counties, 1001 Connecticut Avenue, N.W., Washington, D.C. 20036.

Conservation Commissions in Massachusetts: Stimulating report on how commissions have prompted local action. By Andrew J. W. Scheffey. With supplementary report by William J. Duddleson on spread of conservation commission movement to other states. Published by The Conservation Foundation. 218 p. $3.00. Available from New England Conservation Services Center, South Great Road, Lincoln, Massachusetts 01773.

Conservation Directory: Listing of principal national and state organizations, public and private. $1.50 a copy. Published by National Wildlife Federation, 1412 16th Street, N.W., Washington, D.C. 20036.

County Action for Outdoor Recreation: Forty-eight-page guide on practical steps for county park and recreational programs. Available for 25¢ a copy from the National Association of Counties, 1001 Connecticut Avenue, N.W., Washington, D.C. 20036.

The Electric Utility Industry and the Environment: A report to the Citizens Advisory Committee by a utility industry task force. Offers guidelines on better design of transmission lines, undergrounding of distribution lines, urban siting of nuclear plants, and other environmental challenges. 1968. 105 p. $2.00. Available from Electric Utility Industry Task Force, Room 5600, 30 Rockefeller Plaza, New York, New York 10020.

Federal Assistance in Outdoor Recreation: Summarizes programs of thirty federal agencies for cost-sharing, credit, technical aid, educational services, and research which are available to state, local governments, organizations, and individuals. Prepared by the Bureau of Outdoor Recreation. 1968. 99 p. 35¢ a copy. Government Printing Office, Washington, D.C. 20402.

How to Preserve Your Area for Its Natural Value: Suggestions for landowners. 1962. 8 p. Available free from The Nature Conservancy, 2039 K Street, N.W., Washington, D.C. 20006.

A Little About Lots: Excellent manual on how to make vest pocket parks of vacant lots, organize tree planting and neighborhood clean-up programs. 1969. 62 p. 50¢. Available from the Park Association of New York City, 15 Gramercy Park South, New York, New York 10003.

Manual for Municipal Conservation Commissions: Includes practical suggestions for specific projects. Available free from the Massachusetts Department of Natural Resources, 100 Cambridge Street, Boston, Massachusetts.

More Attractive Communities for California: A practical handbook for community action for a better everyday environment. It is particularly helpful on landscaping techniques. $1.00 a copy. California Roadside Council, 2636 Ocean Avenue, San Francisco, California 94132.

A Nature Center for Your Community: A basic handbook on the values, objectives, elements, and costs of a community nature center and how to go about establishing one. 1962. 40 p. $1.00 a copy. National Audubon Society, 1130 Fifth Avenue, New York, New York 10028.

Open Space for Urban America: By Ann Louise Strong. An excellent and very complete guide to all of the techniques available for conserving open space; extensive appendices include model statutes and legal forms. Free. Available from Office of Metropolitan Development, Department of Housing and Urban Development, Washington, D.C. 20410.

Planning in the Community: A useful checklist of the basic elements of successful local planning efforts. 33 p. 75¢ a copy. League of Women Voters of the United States, 1730 M Street, N.W., Washington, D.C. 20036.

Pollution by Pesticides: Some alternatives for better regulation. 50¢. The Conservation Foundation, 1250 Connecticut Avenue, N.W., Washington, D.C. 20036.

Power Lines and Scenic Values: How to pattern utility rights of way to the landscape. Free. Available from the Hudson River Valley Commission, 105 White Plains Road, Tarrytown, New York 10591.

Recreation and Parks: Case Studies in Local Program: Down-to-earth reports on how thirteen League of Women Voters groups appraised their areas' needs and worked with local officials, other citizens groups, and the voting public toward meeting them. 45¢ a copy. League of Women Voters of the United States, 1200 17th Street, N.W., Washington, D.C. 20036.

Signs Out of Control: Practical suggestions for solving billboard and other sign problems. 75¢. California Roadside Council, 2636 Ocean Avenue, San Francisco, California 94132.

So You'd Like to Do Something About Water Pollution: Concise guide for citizen action, with list of publications and films available. 20¢. League of Women Voters of the United States, 1730 M Street, N.W., Washington, D.C. 20026.

Solid Waste Management: Excellent series on new approaches to waste disposal, with strong emphasis on area-wide action possibilities. Free. National Association of Counties, 1001 Connecticut Avenue, N.W., Washington, D.C. 20036.

Stewardship: Manual for showing landowners how they can conserve open space through gifts of land and of rights in land, and the legal and tax considerations involved. It has been very effective in the New York metropolitan region and should be helpful in any local open space program. $3.00 a copy. Available from the Open Space Institute, 145 E. 52nd Street, New York, New York 10022.

Successful Bond Election Campaigns: Outlines ways to promote support of municipal bond issues. Free. Available from Portland Cement Association, Old Orchard Road, Skokie, Illinois 60076.

Where Not to Build: How to provide open space in the face of urban growth. 1968. 160 p. Technical Bulletin 1, Bureau of Land Management, Department of the Interior. $1.00. Available from U. S. Government Printing Office, Washington, D.C. 20402.

Wildlife Habitat Improvement: A clear, well-illustrated citizen's guide to the management and increasing of wildlife in urban, suburban, and rural areas. 1966. 97 p. $2.50. Available from National Audubon Society, 1130 Fifth Avenue, New York, New York 10028.

Workbook for Clean Air: Instructive booklet on what citizens can do to spur action in their communities. Free. Available from The Conservation Foundation, 1250 Connecticut Avenue, N.W., Washington, D.C. 20036.

Youth Takes the Lead: Lessons of the many community programs sparked by the National Youth Conference on National Beauty and Conservation. $1.95. Available from Urban Research Corporation, 5464 South Shore Drive, Chicago, Illinois 60615.

I